Non-verbal Reasoning
Progress Papers 1

Rebecca Brant

Schofield & Sims

Introduction

The **Non-verbal Reasoning Progress Papers** provide structured activities that increase in difficulty throughout the series, developing your knowledge and skills in non-verbal reasoning. Use the books to prepare for school entrance examinations and to improve your non-verbal reasoning skills.

How to use this book

There are seven papers in this book. Each contains 50 questions, divided by topic into sets of five. The 10 most common types of non-verbal reasoning question are featured in each test paper.

Read through the **Example questions** on pages 4 and 5. Work out why each answer given is correct and then move on to the test papers. Each question in the book is a multiple-choice question. Look closely at the question and its answer options, then draw a ring around the letter option you think is correct.

A single paper may take between 45 and 75 minutes to complete, and you might need two or more sessions to complete one paper.

* For exam preparation, revision and all-round practice, you may choose to work through the papers in numerical order. Once you have completed a paper, ask a teacher, parent or adult helper to correct any mistakes and to explain where you went wrong.

* To practise a topic that you find particularly challenging, you can concentrate on one area and use topic-based material to proceed through the exercises in order of difficulty.

Answers

The answers to all the questions in this book can be found in a pull-out section in the middle. You (or an adult) should use this to mark your work at the end of each paper. You will receive one mark for each correct answer, giving you a total mark out of 50 for every paper. Take time to learn and remember why the answer given is correct.

Use the **Progress chart** at the back of this book to record your marks and measure progress.

Downloads

Free downloads are available from the Schofield & Sims website (www.schofieldandsims.co.uk/free-downloads), including extra practice material.

Published by **Schofield & Sims Ltd**
Dogley Mill, Fenay Bridge, Huddersfield HD8 0NQ, UK
Telephone 01484 607080
www.schofieldandsims.co.uk
First published in 2016
This edition copyright © Schofield & Sims Ltd, 2018

Author: **Rebecca Brant**
Rebecca Brant has asserted her moral rights under the Copyright, Designs and Patents Act, 1988, to be identified as the author of this work.

British Library Cataloguing in Publication Data
A catalogue record for this book is available from the British Library.

Design by **Oxford Designers & Illustrators**
Cover design by **Ledgard Jepson Ltd**
Printed in the UK by **Page Bros (Norwich) Ltd**

ISBN 978 07217 1460 8

Contents

Note for parents, tutors, teachers and other adult helpers
A pull-out answers section (pages A1 to A12) appears in the centre of this book, between pages 28 and 29 (Paper 4). This provides answers to all the questions, along with guidance on marking the papers. Remove the pull-out section before the child begins working through the practice papers. The child should have access to a spare piece of paper for the nets of cubes questions if needed.

Example questions

Similarities

Which picture on the right belongs to the group on the left? Circle the letter.

Example

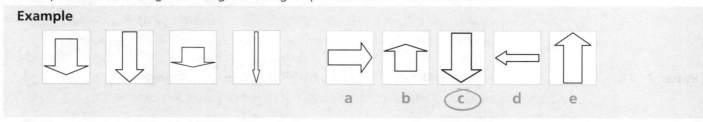

Analogies

Which of the five pictures on the right goes with the third one to make a pair like the two on the left? Circle the letter.

Example

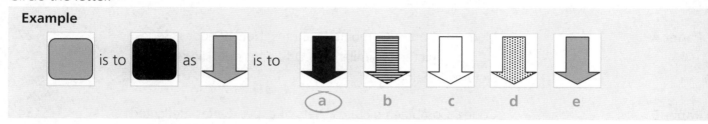

Matrices

Which picture on the right best fits into the space in the grid? Circle the letter.

Example

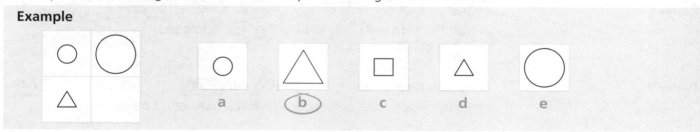

Hidden pictures

In which picture on the right is the picture on the left hidden? Circle the letter.

Example

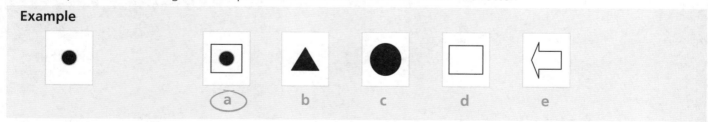

Odd ones out

Which picture is the odd one out? Circle the letter.

Example

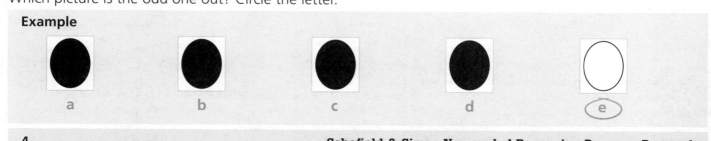

Reflected pictures

Which picture on the right is a reflection of the picture on the left? Circle the letter.

Example

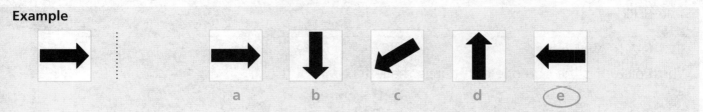

Codes

What is the code of the final picture? Circle the letter.

Example

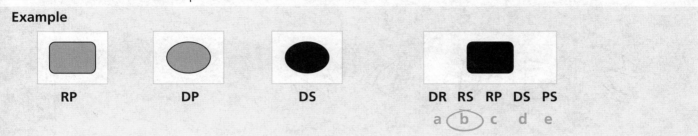

Combined pictures

Which picture on the right can be made by combining the first two pictures? Circle the letter.

Example

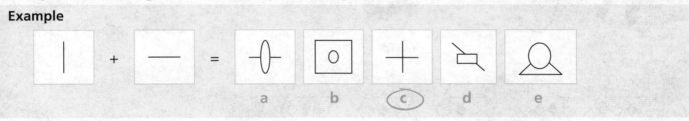

Nets of cubes

Which cube can be made exactly from the net? Circle the letter.

Example

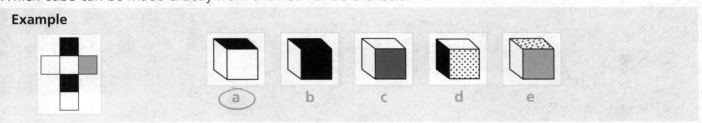

Which net can be made exactly from the cube? Circle the letter.

Example

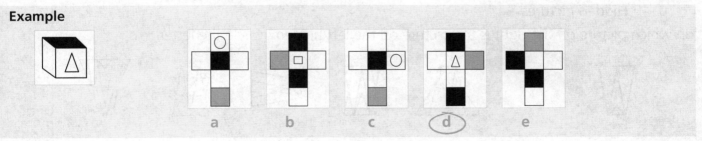

Series

Which picture on the right fits in the empty space? Circle the letter.

Example

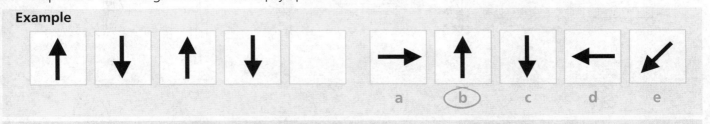

START HERE

Q. 1–5 Odd ones out

Which picture is the odd one out? Circle the letter.

1

a   b   c   d   e

1 ☐

2

a   b   c   d   e

2 ☐

3

a   b   c   d   e

3 ☐

4

a   b   c   d   e

4 ☐

5

a   b   c   d   e

5 ☐

Q. 6–10 Hidden pictures

In which picture on the right is the picture on the left hidden? Circle the letter.

6

a   b   c   d   e

6 ☐

7

a   b   c   d   e

7 ☐

MARK ☐

MARK
✓ OR ✗

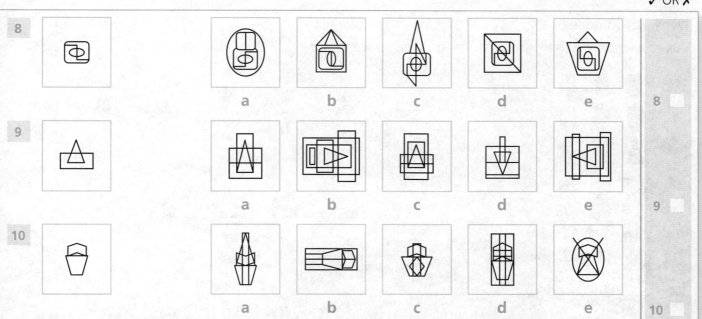

8

a   b   c   d   e   8 ☐

9

a   b   c   d   e   9 ☐

10

a   b   c   d   e   10 ☐

Q. 11–15 Analogies

Which of the five pictures on the right goes with the third one to make a pair like the two on the left? Circle the letter.

11   is to   as   is to   a   b   c   d   e   11 ☐

12   is to   as   is to   a   b   c   d   e   12 ☐

13   is to   as   is to   a   b   c   d   e   13 ☐

14   is to   as   is to   a   b   c   d   e   14 ☐

15   is to   as   is to   a   b   c   d   e   15 ☐

MARK ☐

MARK
✓ OR ✗

Q. 16–20 Matrices

Which picture on the right best fits into the space in the grid? Circle the letter.

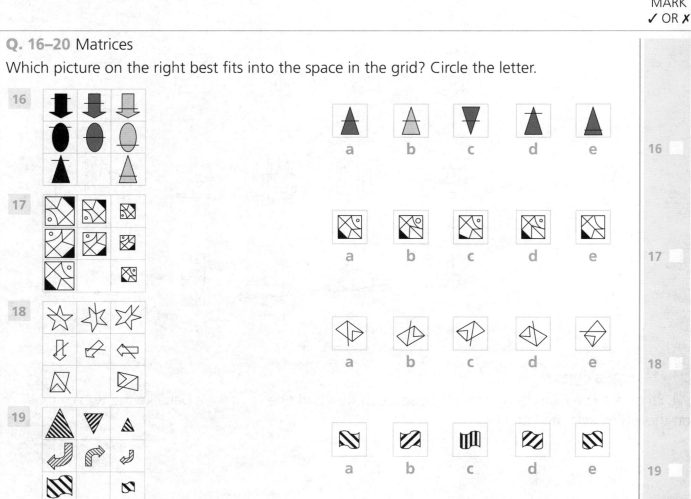

16

17

18

19

20

Q. 21–25 Codes

What is the code of the final picture? Circle the letter.

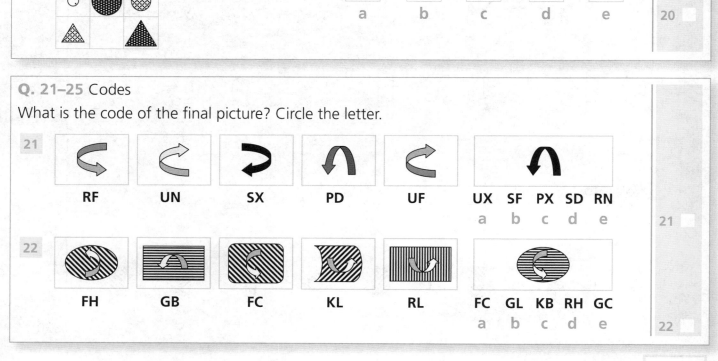

21

22

MARK

Schofield & Sims • Non-verbal Reasoning Progress Papers 1

MARK
✓ OR ✗

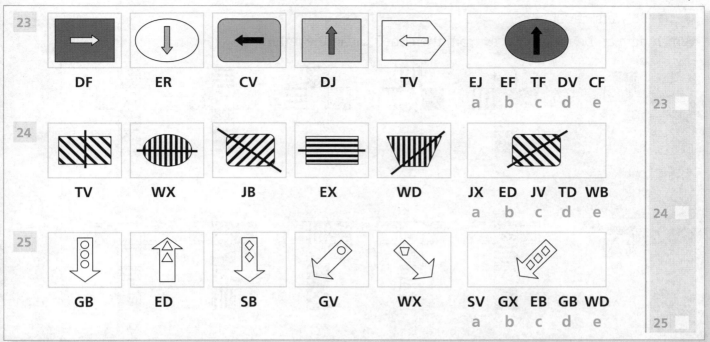

23   DF   ER   CV   DJ   TV   EJ   EF   TF   DV   CF
                                          a   b   c   d   e   23 ☐

24   TV   WX   JB   EX   WD   JX   ED   JV   TD   WB
                                          a   b   c   d   e   24 ☐

25   GB   ED   SB   GV   WX   SV   GX   EB   GB   WD
                                          a   b   c   d   e   25 ☐

Q. 26–30 Combined pictures

Which picture on the right can be made by combining the first two pictures? Circle the letter.

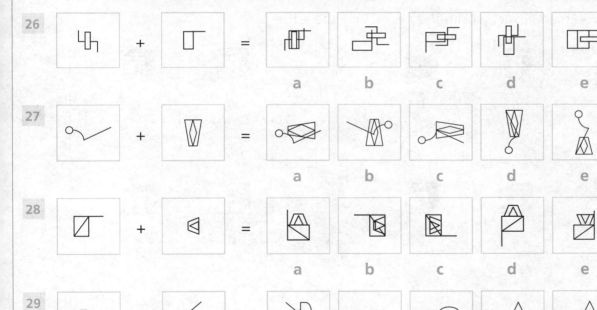

26   +   =   a   b   c   d   e   26 ☐

27   +   =   a   b   c   d   e   27 ☐

28   +   =   a   b   c   d   e   28 ☐

29   +   =   a   b   c   d   e   29 ☐

30   +   =   a   b   c   d   e   30 ☐

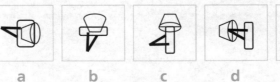

MARK ☐

MARK
✓ OR ✗

Q. 31–35 Nets of cubes

Which net can be made exactly from the cube? Circle the letter.

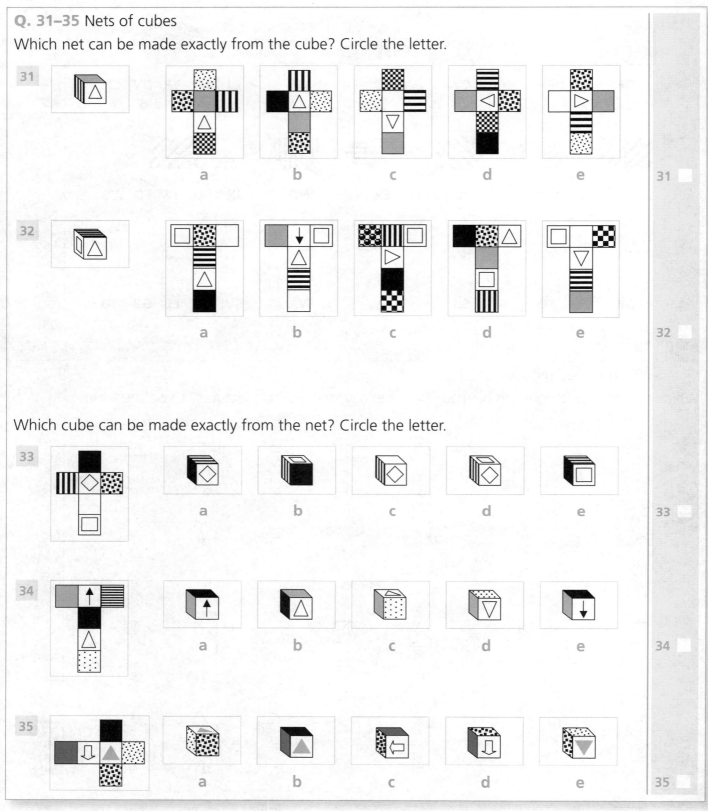

31

a   b   c   d   e

31 ☐

32

a   b   c   d   e

32 ☐

Which cube can be made exactly from the net? Circle the letter.

33

a   b   c   d   e

33 ☐

34

a   b   c   d   e

34 ☐

35

a   b   c   d   e

35 ☐

MARK ☐

MARK
✓ OR ✗

Q. 36–40 Series

Which picture on the right fits in the empty space? Circle the letter.

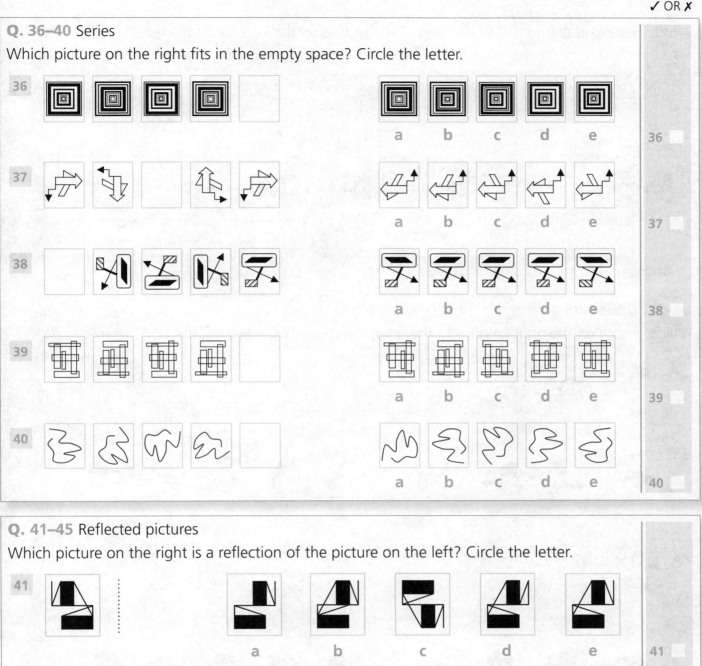

36

36

37

a   b   c   d   e

37

38

a   b   c   d   e

38

39

a   b   c   d   e

39

40

a   b   c   d   e

40

Q. 41–45 Reflected pictures

Which picture on the right is a reflection of the picture on the left? Circle the letter.

41

a   b   c   d   e

41

42

a   b   c   d   e

42

43

a   b   c   d   e

43

MARK

MARK
✓ OR ✗

Which picture on the right is a reflection of the picture on the left? Circle the letter.

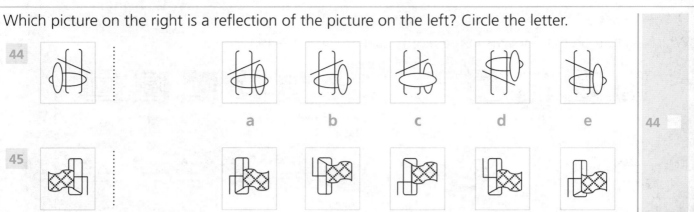

44 | | |
45 | | |

Q. 46–50 Similarities

Which picture on the right belongs to the group on the left? Circle the letter.

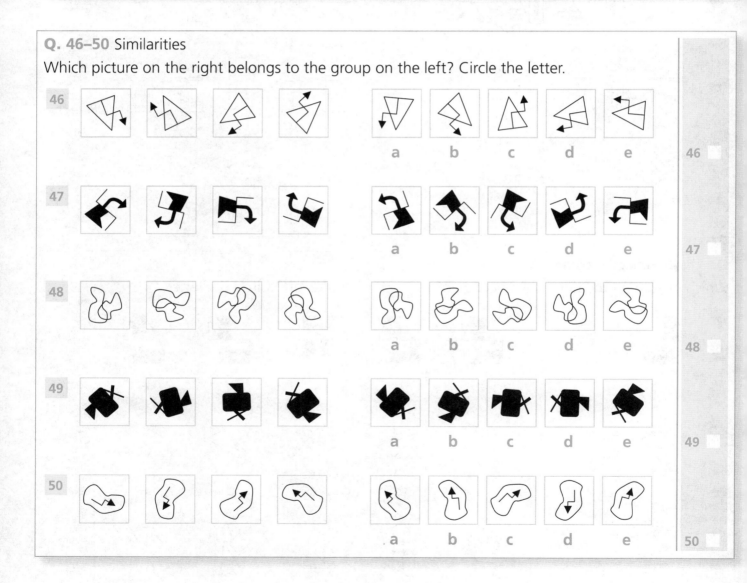

46
47
48
49
50

MARK

END OF TEST

PAPER 1 TOTAL MARK

START HERE

Q. 1–5 Hidden pictures

In which picture on the right is the picture on the left hidden? Circle the letter.

1

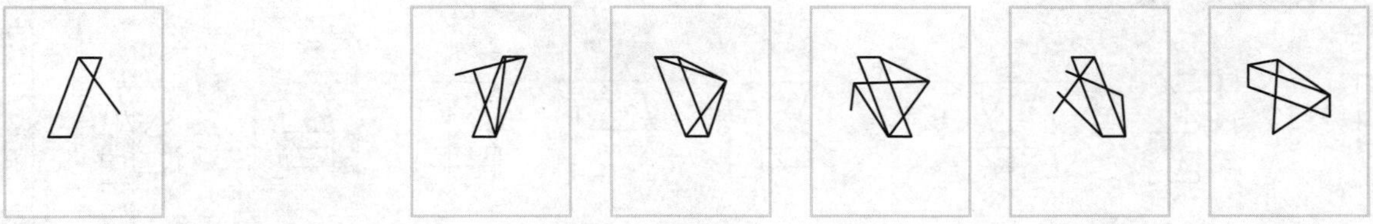

       a   b   c   d   e   1 ☐

2

       a   b   c   d   e   2 ☐

3

       a   b   c   d   e   3 ☐

4    

       a   b   c   d   e   4 ☐

5   

       a   b   c   d   e   5 ☐

MARK ☐

MARK
✓ OR ✗

Q. 6–10 Analogies

Which of the five pictures on the right goes with the third one to make a pair like the two on the left? Circle the letter.

6 is to as is to

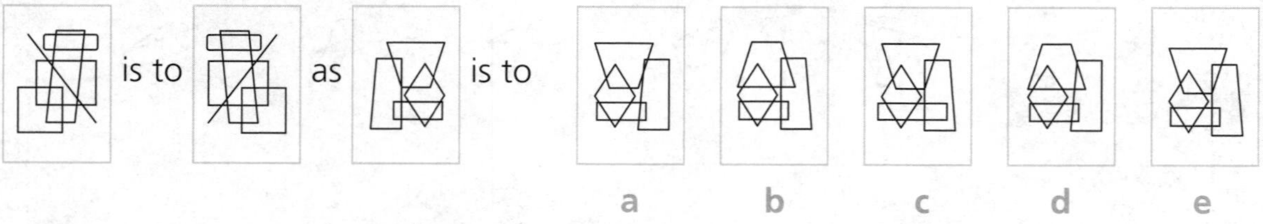

     a   b   c   d   e   **6** ☐

7 is to as is to

     a   b   c   d   e   **7** ☐

8 is to as is to

     a   b   c   d   e   **8** ☐

9 is to as is to

     a   b   c   d   e   **9** ☐

10 is to as is to

     a   b   c   d   e   **10** ☐

MARK ☐

MARK
✓ OR ✗

Q. 11–15 Matrices

Which picture on the right best fits into the space in the grid? Circle the letter.

11

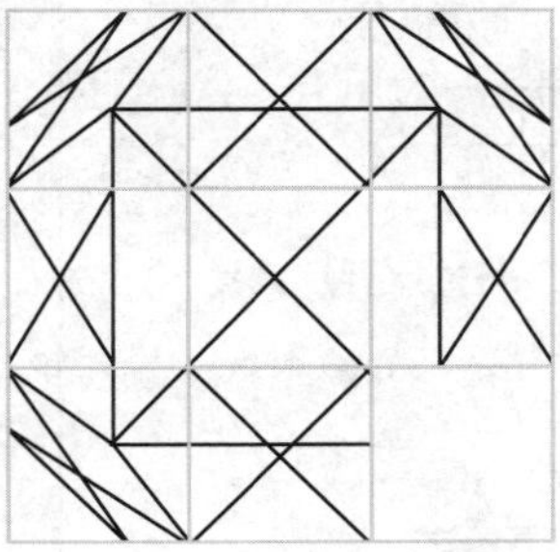

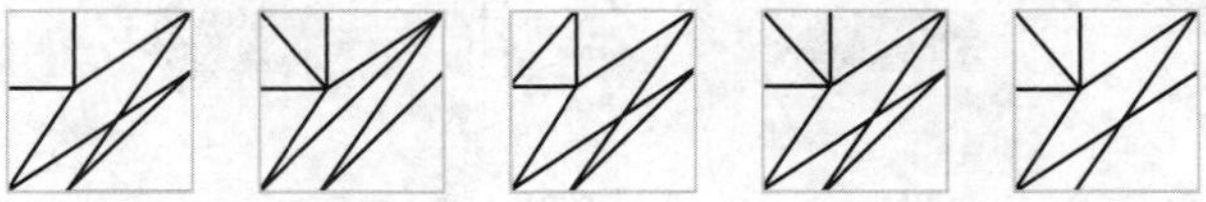

a b c d e

11

12

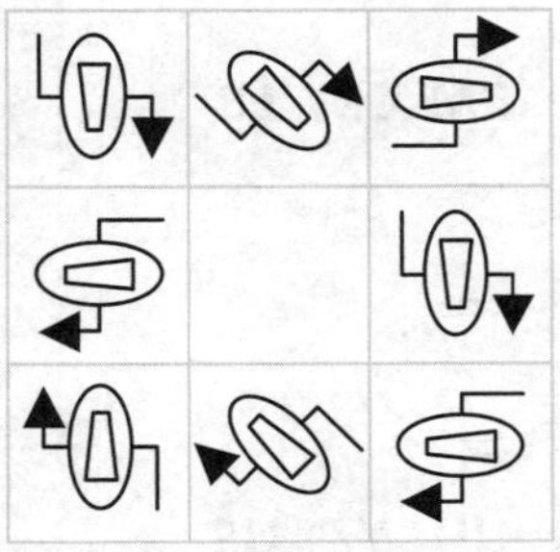

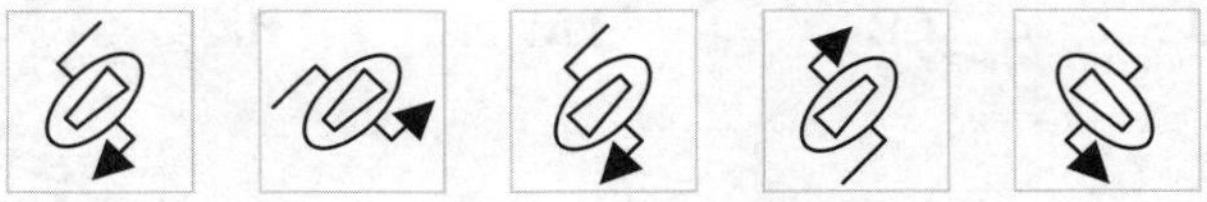

a b c d e

12

13

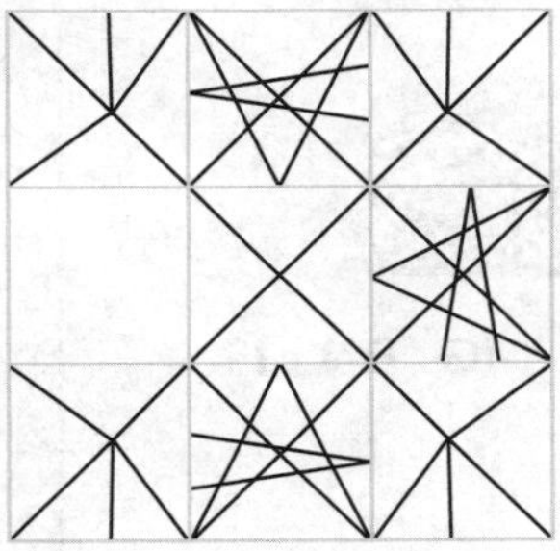

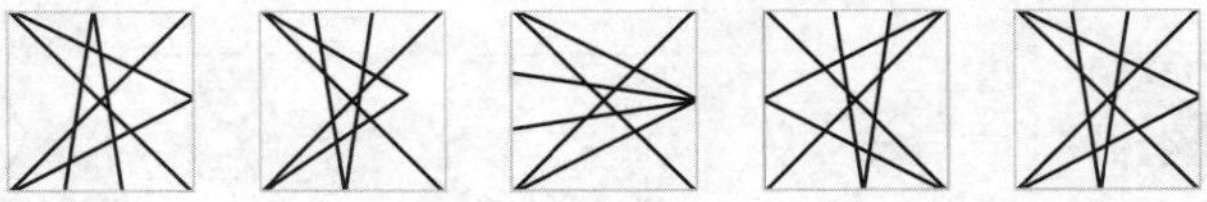

a b c d e

13

14

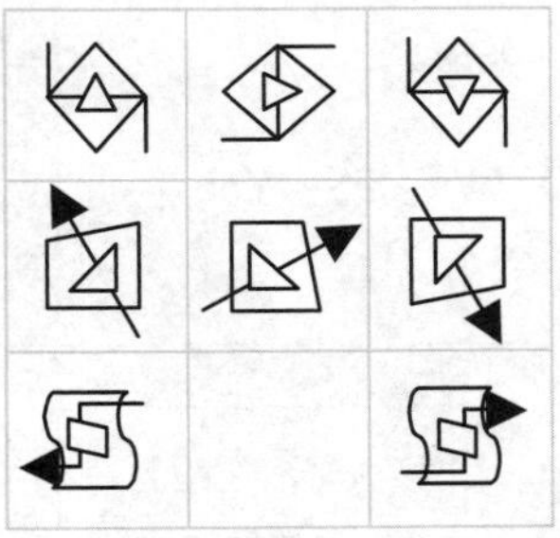

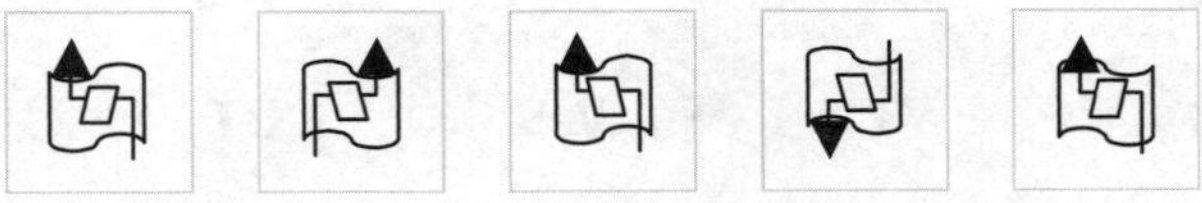

a b c d e

14

15

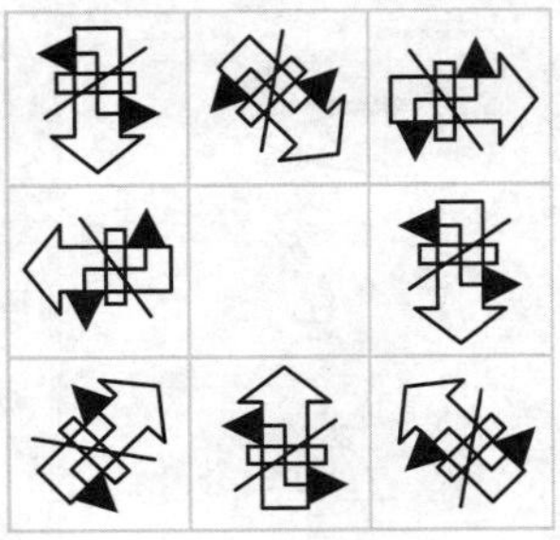

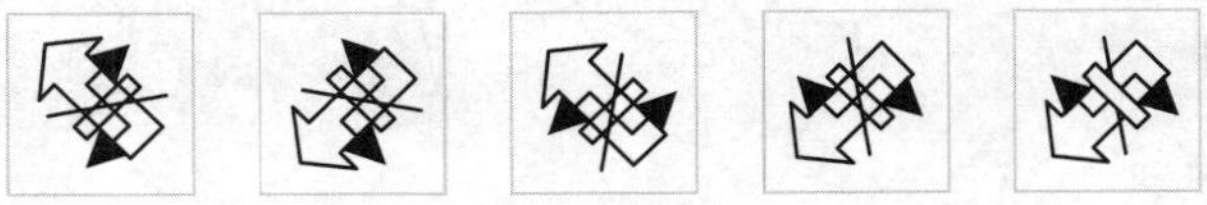

a b c d e

15

MARK

MARK
✓ OR ✗

Q. 16–20 Codes

What is the code of the final picture? Circle the letter.

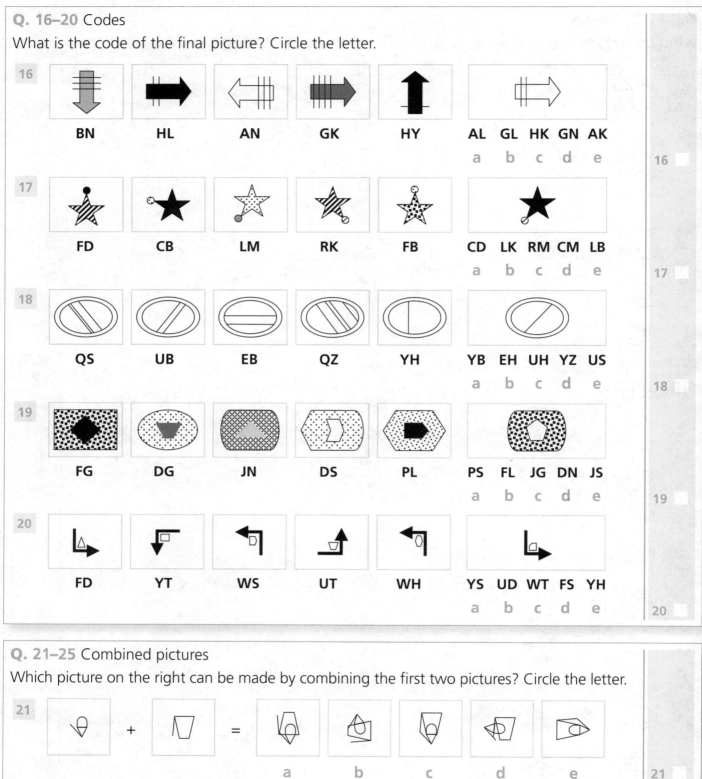

16

BN   HL   AN   GK   HY   AL GL HK GN AK
a b c d e

16 ☐

17

FD   CB   LM   RK   FB   CD LK RM CM LB
a b c d e

17 ☐

18

QS   UB   EB   QZ   YH   YB EH UH YZ US
a b c d e

18 ☐

19

FG   DG   JN   DS   PL   PS FL JG DN JS
a b c d e

19 ☐

20

FD   YT   WS   UT   WH   YS UD WT FS YH
a b c d e

20 ☐

Q. 21–25 Combined pictures

Which picture on the right can be made by combining the first two pictures? Circle the letter.

21

a   b   c   d   e

21 ☐

22

a   b   c   d   e

22 ☐

MARK ☐

MARK
✓ OR ✗

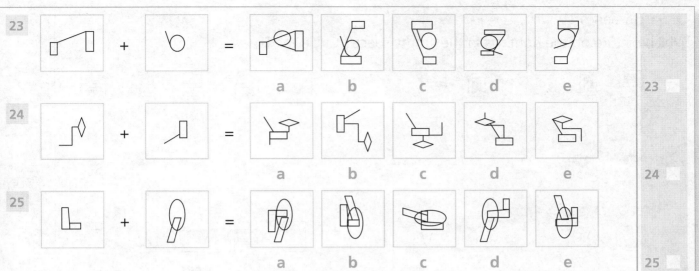

Q. 26–30 Nets of cubes

Which net can be made exactly from the cube? Circle the letter.

Which cube can be made exactly from the net? Circle the letter.

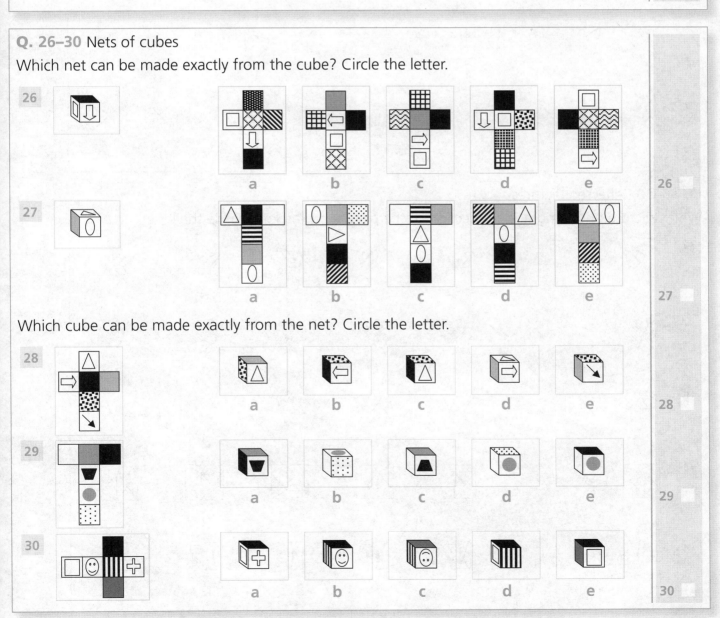

MARK

MARK
✓ OR ✗

Q. 31–35 Series

Which picture on the right fits in the empty space? Circle the letter.

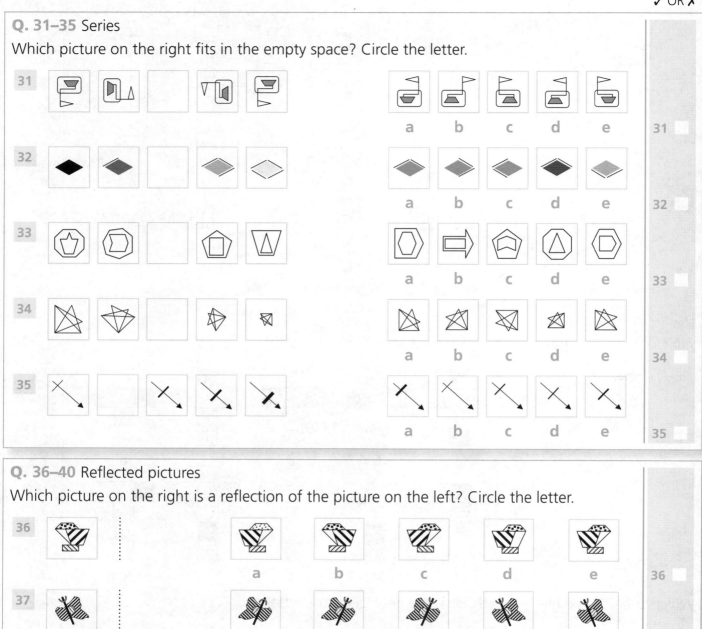

31	
32	
33	
34	
35	

Q. 36–40 Reflected pictures

Which picture on the right is a reflection of the picture on the left? Circle the letter.

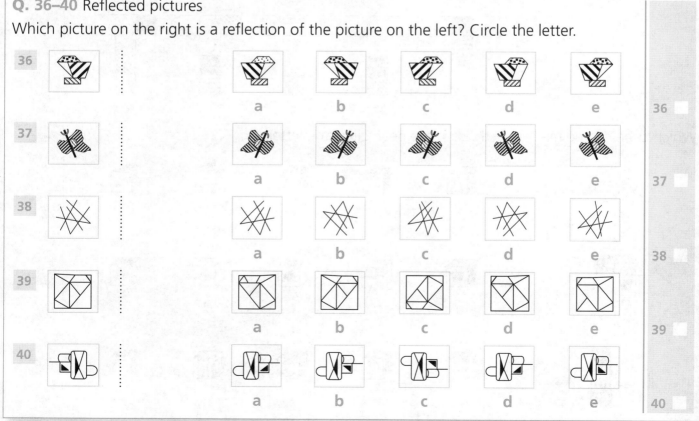

36	
37	
38	
39	
40	

MARK ☐

Schofield & Sims · Non-verbal Reasoning Progress Papers 1

MARK
✓ OR ✗

Q. 41–45 Similarities

Which picture on the right belongs to the group on the left? Circle the letter.

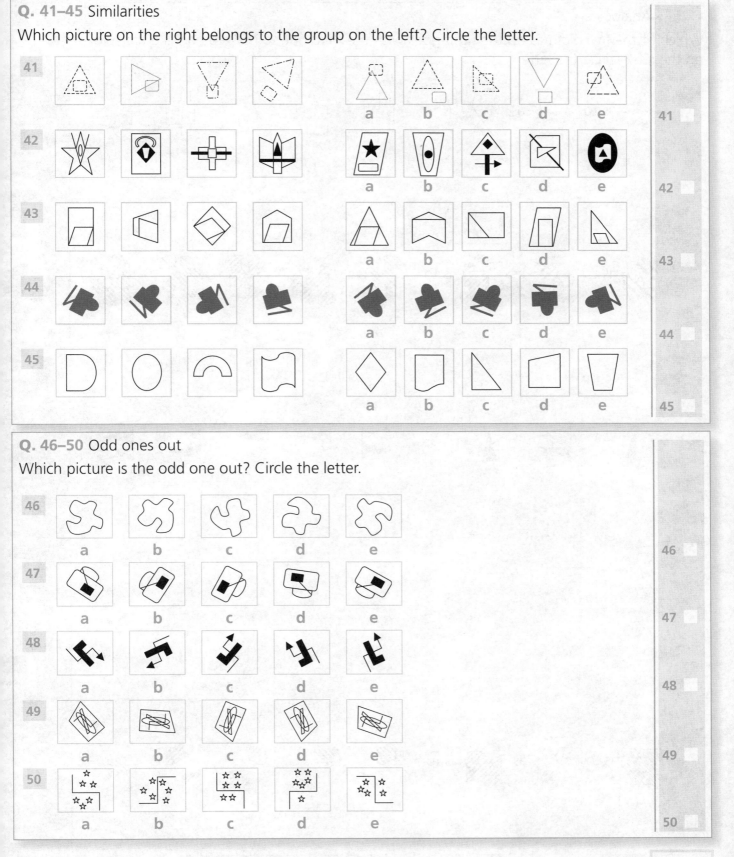

Q. 46–50 Odd ones out

Which picture is the odd one out? Circle the letter.

START HERE

Q. 1–5 Analogies

Which of the five pictures on the right goes with the third one to make a pair like the two on the left? Circle the letter.

1 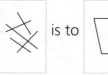 is to as is to

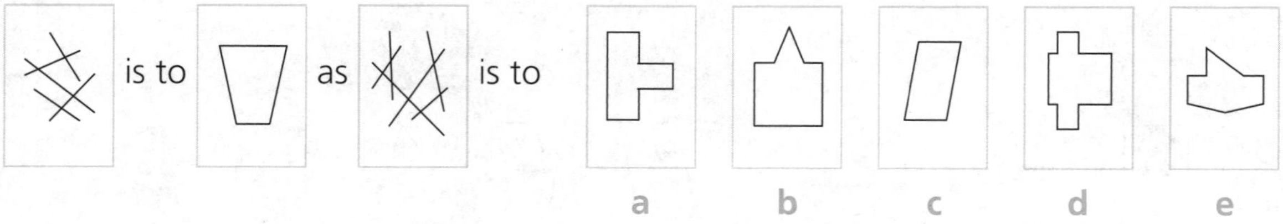

          a   b   c   d   e   1 ☐

2 is to as  is to

          a   b   c   d   e   2 ☐

3 is to as is to

          a   b   c   d   e   3 ☐

4 is to as is to

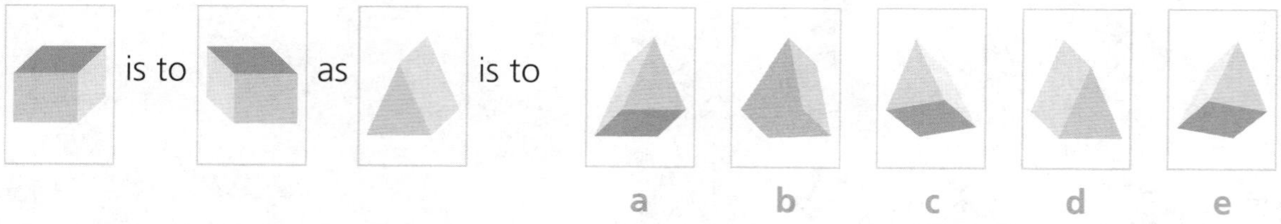

          a   b   c   d   e   4 ☐

5 is to as is to

          a   b   c   d   e   5 ☐

MARK ☐

MARK
✓ OR ✗

Q. 6–10 Matrices

Which picture on the right best fits into the space in the grid? Circle the letter.

6

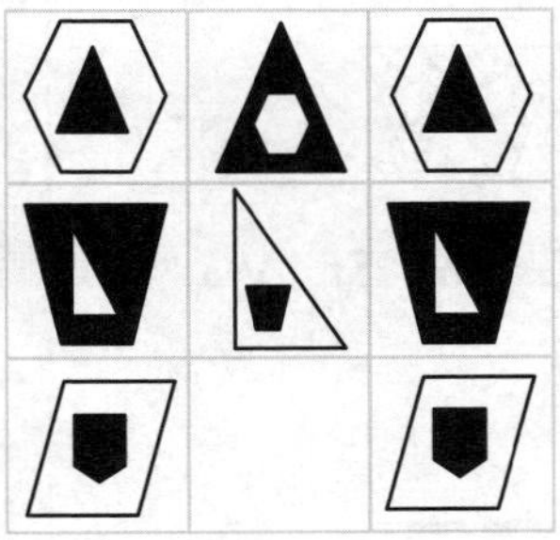

a   b   c   d   e

6 ☐

7

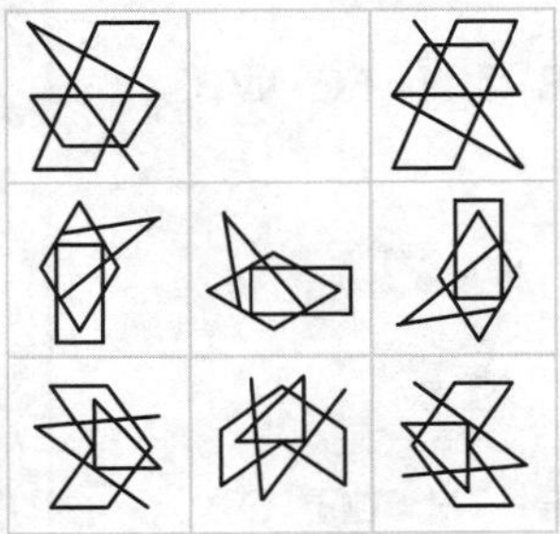

a   b   c   d   e

7 ☐

8

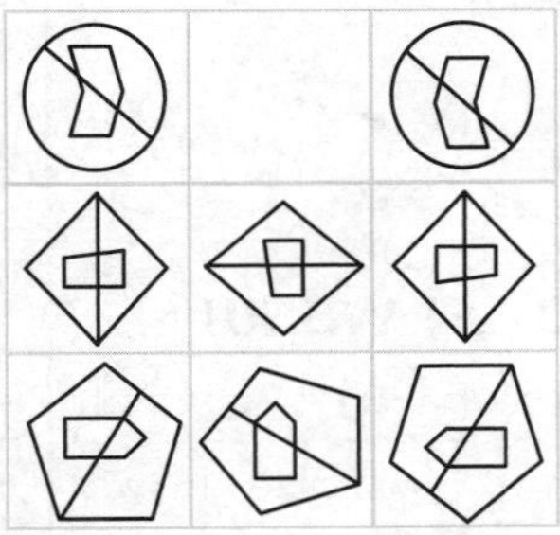

a   b   c   d   e

8 ☐

9

a   b   c   d   e

9 ☐

10

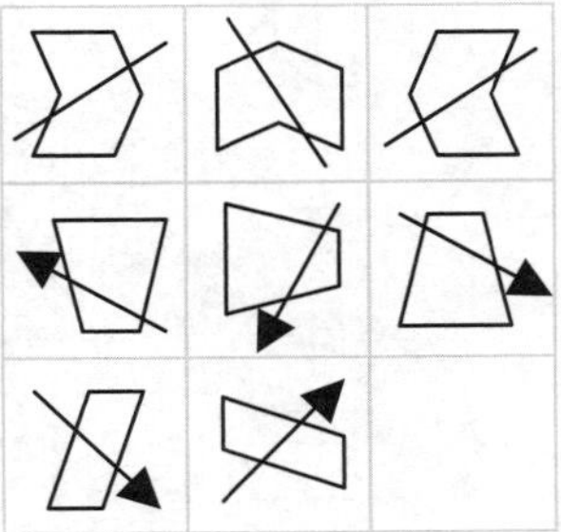

a   b   c   d   e

10 ☐

MARK ☐

MARK
✓ OR ✗

Q. 11–15 Codes

What is the code of the final picture? Circle the letter.

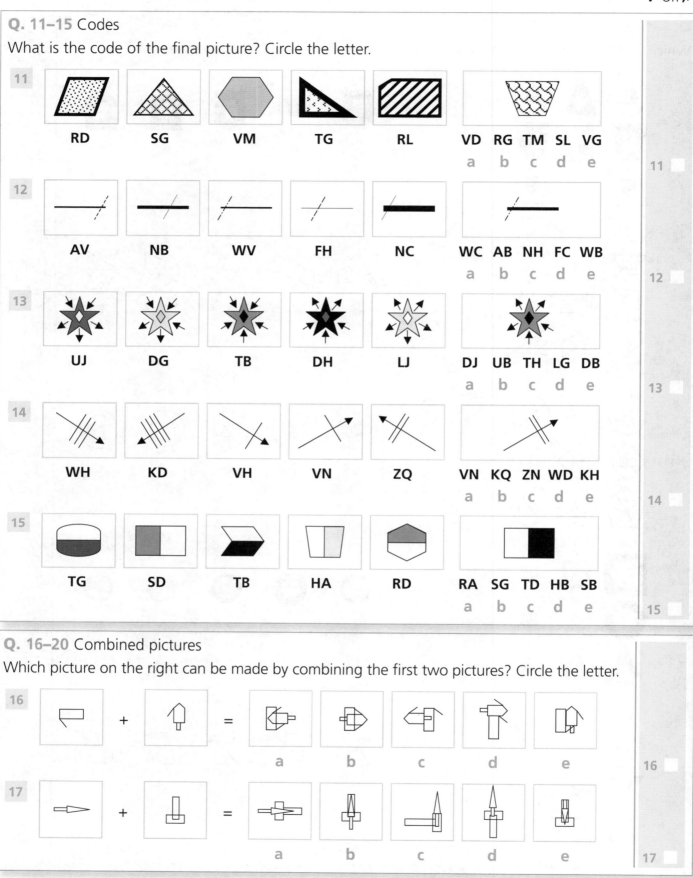

11

RD SG VM TG RL VD RG TM SL VG
               a b c d e

11 ☐

12

AV NB WV FH NC WC AB NH FC WB
               a b c d e

12 ☐

13

UJ DG TB DH LJ DJ UB TH LG DB
               a b c d e

13 ☐

14

WH KD VH VN ZQ VN KQ ZN WD KH
               a b c d e

14 ☐

15

TG SD TB HA RD RA SG TD HB SB
               a b c d e

15 ☐

Q. 16–20 Combined pictures

Which picture on the right can be made by combining the first two pictures? Circle the letter.

16

             a   b   c   d   e

16 ☐

17

             a   b   c   d   e

17 ☐

MARK ☐

MARK
✓ OR ✗

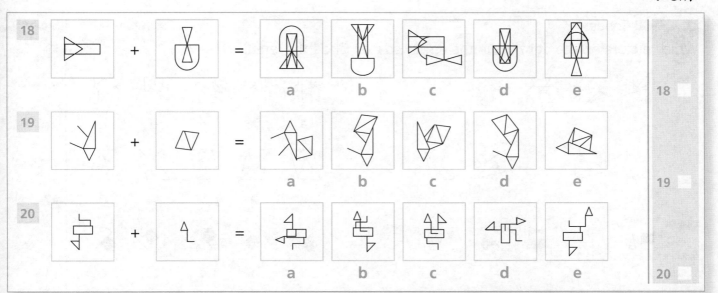

18 | 18 ☐

19 | 19 ☐

20 | 20 ☐

Q. 21–25 Nets of cubes

Which net can be made exactly from the cube? Circle the letter.

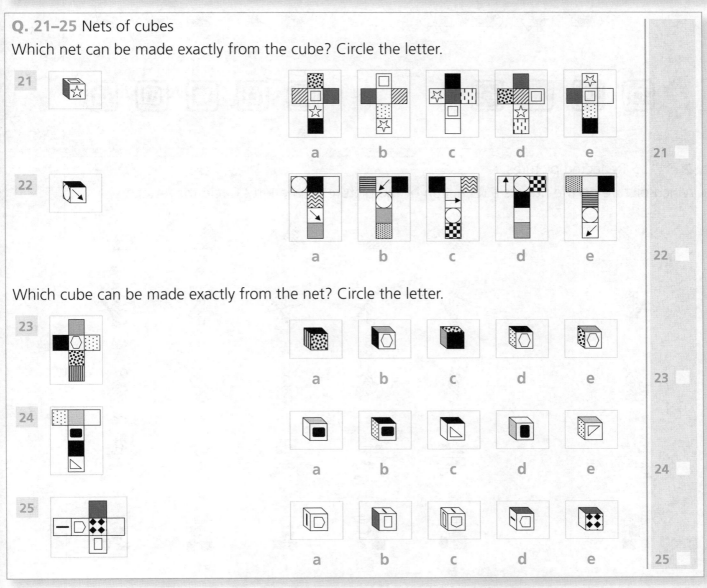

Which cube can be made exactly from the net? Circle the letter.

21 | 21 ☐
22 | 22 ☐
23 | 23 ☐
24 | 24 ☐
25 | 25 ☐

MARK ☐

MARK
✓ OR ✗

Q. 26–30 Series

Which picture on the right fits in the empty space? Circle the letter.

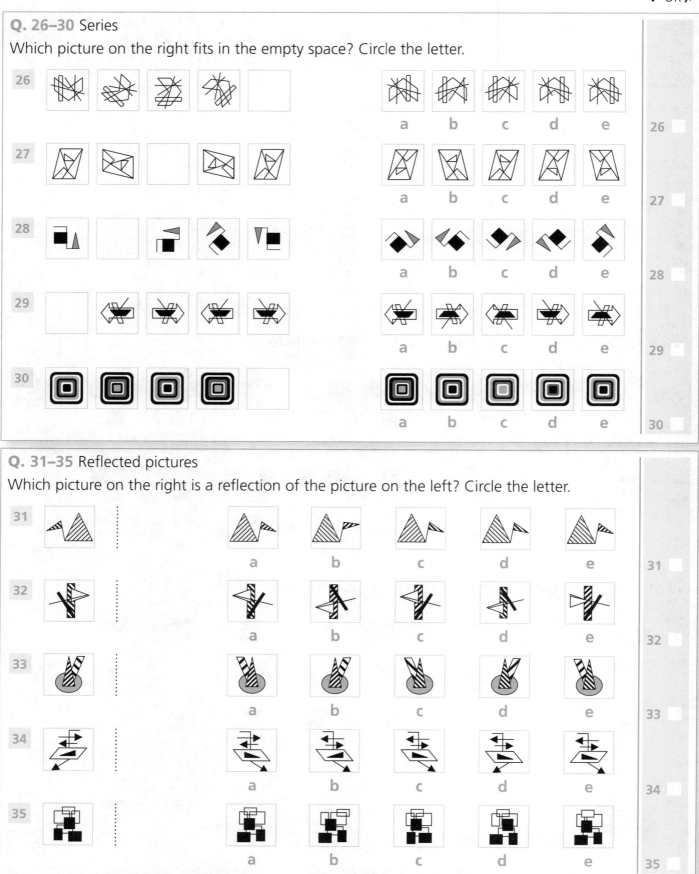

26

a   b   c   d   e   26 ☐

27

a   b   c   d   e   27 ☐

28

a   b   c   d   e   28 ☐

29

a   b   c   d   e   29 ☐

30

a   b   c   d   e   30 ☐

Q. 31–35 Reflected pictures

Which picture on the right is a reflection of the picture on the left? Circle the letter.

31

a   b   c   d   e   31 ☐

32

a   b   c   d   e   32 ☐

33

a   b   c   d   e   33 ☐

34

a   b   c   d   e   34 ☐

35

a   b   c   d   e   35 ☐

MARK ☐

MARK
✓ OR ✗

Q. 36–40 Similarities

Which picture on the right belongs to the group on the left? Circle the letter.

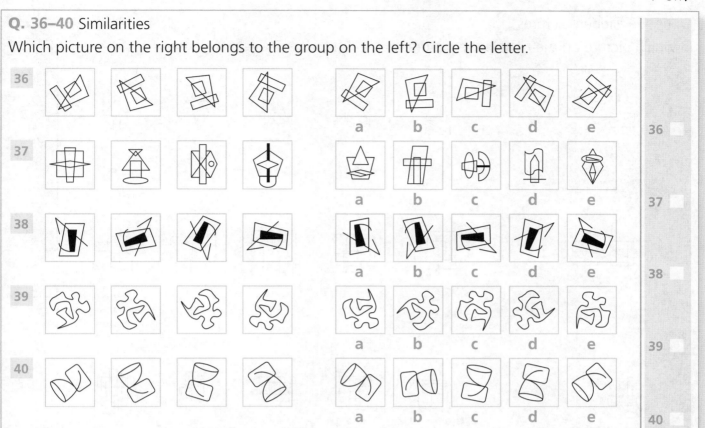

36

37

38

39

40

Q. 41–45 Odd ones out

Which picture is the odd one out? Circle the letter.

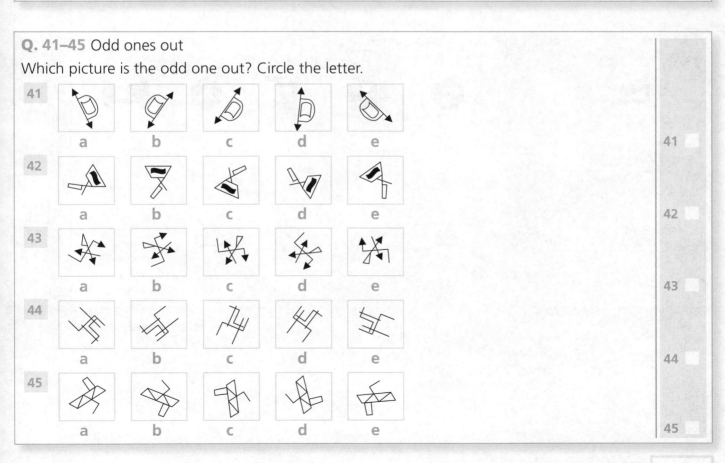

41

42

43

44

45

MARK

MARK
✓ OR ✗

Q. 46–50 Hidden pictures

In which picture on the right is the picture on the left hidden? Circle the letter.

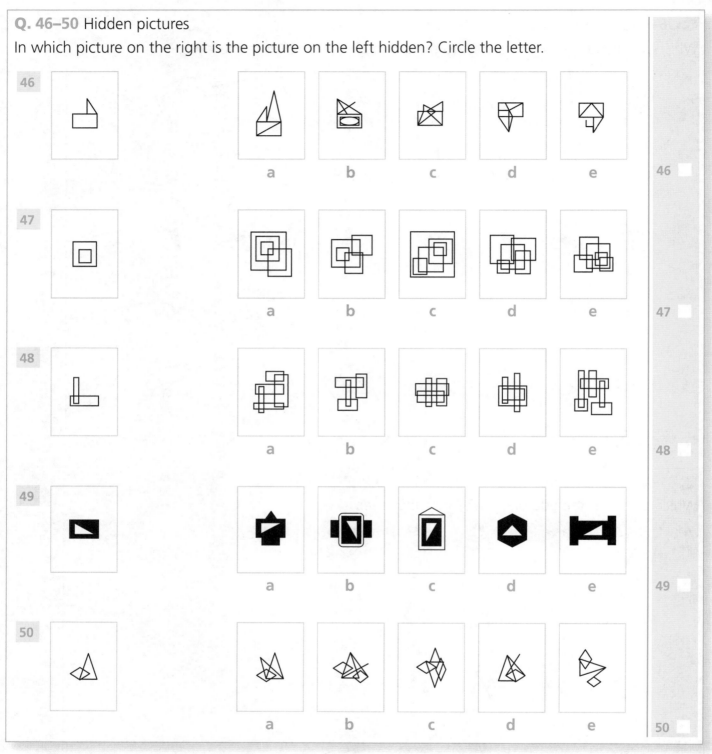

46

| | a | b | c | d | e |

46 ☐

47

| | a | b | c | d | e |

47 ☐

48

| | a | b | c | d | e |

48 ☐

49

| | a | b | c | d | e |

49 ☐

50

| | a | b | c | d | e |

50 ☐

MARK ☐

END OF TEST

PAPER 3 TOTAL MARK ☐

Schofield & Sims • Non-verbal Reasoning Progress Papers 1

START HERE

MARK
✓ OR ✗

Q. 1–5 Matrices

Which picture on the right best fits into the space in the grid? Circle the letter.

1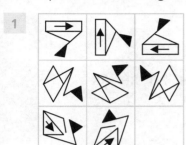

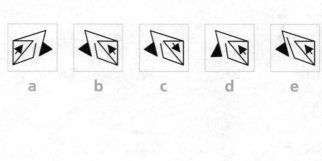

a   b   c   d   e

1 ☐

2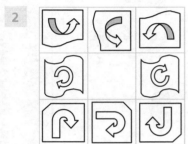

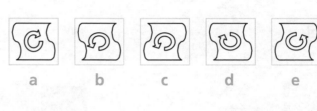

a   b   c   d   e

2 ☐

3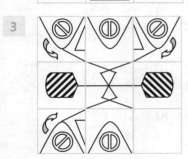

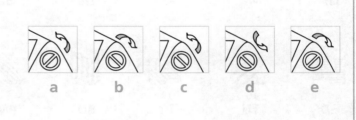

a   b   c   d   e

3 ☐

4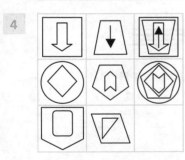

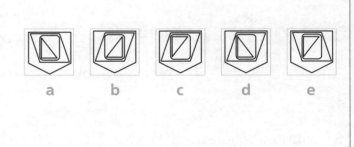

a   b   c   d   e

4 ☐

5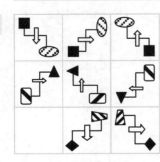

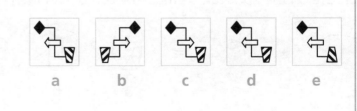

a   b   c   d   e

5 ☐

MARK ☐

MARK
✓ OR ✗

Q. 6–10 Codes

What is the code of the final picture? Circle the letter.

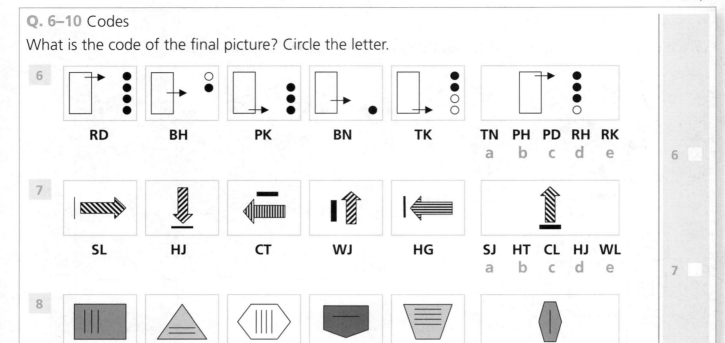

6

| RD | BH | PK | BN | TK | TN | PH | PD | RH | RK |
|----|----|----|----|----| a | b | c | d | e |

6

7

| SL | HJ | CT | WJ | HG | SJ | HT | CL | HJ | WL |
|----|----|----|----|----| a | b | c | d | e |

7

8

| GF | MK | AD | HL | GD | GK | HF | MD | AL | AK |
|----|----|----|----|----| a | b | c | d | e |

8

9

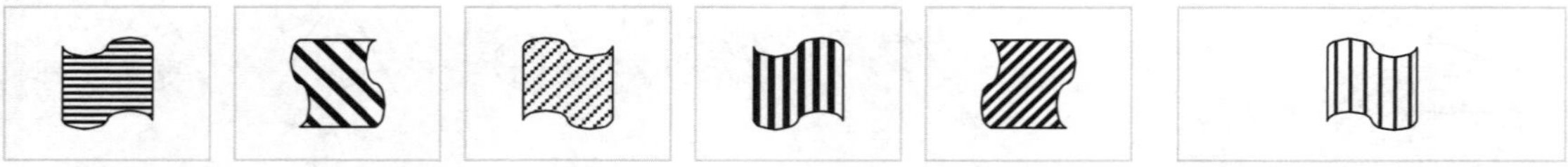

| GD | TU | PZ | BD | PM | PD | TM | BM | GU | BZ |
|----|----|----|----|----| a | b | c | d | e |

9

10

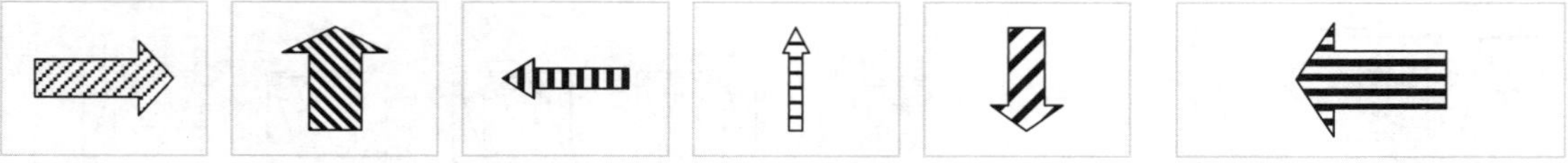

| GH | SV | PM | DV | GK | DM | PV | SK | PH | DH |
|----|----|----|----|----| a | b | c | d | e |

10

Q. 11–15 Combined pictures

Which picture on the right can be made by combining the first two pictures? Circle the letter.

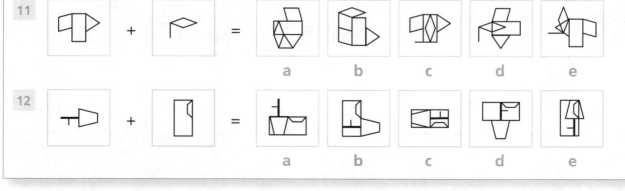

11

a   b   c   d   e

11

12

a   b   c   d   e

12

MARK

Non-verbal Reasoning
Progress Papers 1
Answers

Schofield & Sims

Non-verbal Reasoning Progress Papers 1

Notes for parents, tutors, teachers and other helpers

This pull-out book contains correct answers to all the questions in **Non-verbal Reasoning Progress Papers 1**, and is designed to assist you, the adult helper, as you mark the child's work. Once the child has become accustomed to the method of working, you may wish to give him or her direct access to this pull-out section.

When marking, put a tick or a cross in the tinted column on the far right of the question page. **Only one mark is available for each question**. Sub-total boxes at the foot of each page will help you to add marks quickly. You can then fill in the total marks at the end of the paper. The total score is out of 50 and can easily be turned into a percentage by multiplying the child's mark by two. (For example, a score of 40 multiplied by two gives 80%.) The child's progress can be recorded using the **Progress chart** on page 56.

The child should aim to spend between 45 and 75 minutes on each paper, but may need more time, or more than one session, to complete the paper. The child should try to work on each paper when feeling fresh and free from distraction.

How to use the pull-out answers

This answer booklet contains explanations and colour-coded pictures to help with marking. Where the child has answered a question incorrectly, take time to look at the question and answer together and work out how the correct answer was achieved.

By working through the tests and corresponding answers, the child will start to recognise the clues that he or she should look for next time. For example, the child may learn to analyse changes in pattern, reflection, rotation, size, colour and shape. These skills can then be put into practice by moving on to the next paper, as the difficulty increases incrementally throughout the series.

When a paper has been marked, notice if there are any topics that are proving particularly tricky. You may wish to complete some targeted practice in those areas, by focusing on that particular topic as it appears in each paper. For example, if a child has struggled with nets of cubes, but answered all other questions accurately, you may wish to target only nets of cubes questions in your next practice session. Each paper contains all 10 of the most common types of non-verbal reasoning question, so it is easy to tailor practice to the child's individual needs.

Paper 1

1 | a | The others are all rotations of the same picture.
2 | e | The others are all rotations of the same picture.
3 | c | The other arrows are all turning anticlockwise.
4 | d | The others all have one black, one grey and one white rhombus.
5 | c | The others all have the triangle at the wider end of the trapezium.

6 | a |

7 | c |

8 | d |

9 | b |

10 | b |

11 | d | reflection in the horizontal mirror line; the darker shadow remains on the bottom face of the shape
12 | c | same number of lines as number of stars
13 | e | reflection in the vertical mirror line
14 | c | number of shapes doubles
15 | b | reflection in the vertical mirror line

Paper 1 – continued

16 | a | colour gets gradually lighter and line moves down the shape on each row
17 | a | shape gets smaller
18 | c | shape rotates 45° clockwise
19 | b | shape gets smaller, rotates 180°, line direction reflects
20 | c | each row contains a shape in three different sizes, with three different patterns
21 | c | first letter – arrow direction
second letter – colour
22 | e | first letter – line direction
second letter – arrow direction
23 | a | first letter – outer shape
second letter – arrow direction
24 | d | first letter – internal line direction
second letter – long line direction
25 | a | first letter – internal shape
second letter – arrow direction

26 | e |

27 | d |

28 | a |

29 | e |

30 | d |

Paper 1 – continued

31 | c
32 | a
33 | e
34 | c
35 | c

If in doubt about the nets of cubes, copy them onto a piece of paper and fold them.

36 | d | repeating pattern
37 | b | rotating 90° clockwise
38 | c | rotating 90° clockwise
39 | e | repeating pattern
40 | b | rotating 45° clockwise

41 | e |

42 | e |

43 | a |

44 | b |

45 | a |

46 | d | Each picture is rotation of the same picture.
47 | b | Each picture is rotation of the same picture.
48 | e | Each picture is rotation of the same picture.
49 | c | Each picture is rotation of the same picture.
50 | b | Each picture is rotation of the same picture.

Paper 2

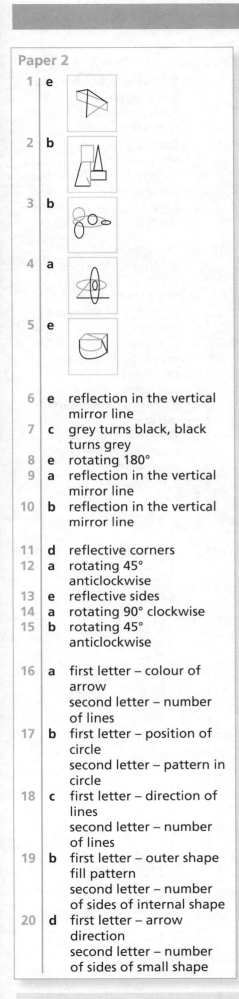

1 e

2 b

3 b

4 a

5 e

6 e reflection in the vertical mirror line
7 c grey turns black, black turns grey
8 e rotating 180°
9 a reflection in the vertical mirror line
10 b reflection in the vertical mirror line

11 d reflective corners
12 a rotating 45° anticlockwise
13 e reflective sides
14 a rotating 90° clockwise
15 b rotating 45° anticlockwise

16 a first letter – colour of arrow
      second letter – number of lines
17 b first letter – position of circle
      second letter – pattern in circle
18 c first letter – direction of lines
      second letter – number of lines
19 b first letter – outer shape fill pattern
      second letter – number of sides of internal shape
20 d first letter – arrow direction
      second letter – number of sides of small shape

Paper 2 – *continued*

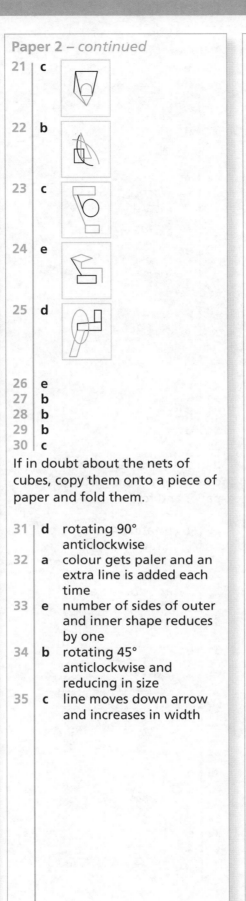

21 c

22 b

23 c

24 e

25 d

26 e
27 b
28 b
29 b
30 c

If in doubt about the nets of cubes, copy them onto a piece of paper and fold them.

31 d rotating 90° anticlockwise
32 a colour gets paler and an extra line is added each time
33 e number of sides of outer and inner shape reduces by one
34 b rotating 45° anticlockwise and reducing in size
35 c line moves down arrow and increases in width

Paper 2 – *continued*

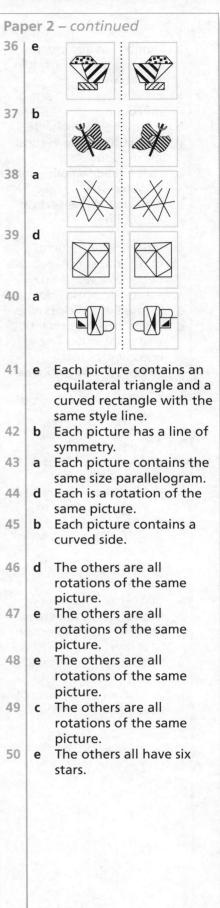

36 e

37 b

38 a

39 d

40 a

41 e Each picture contains an equilateral triangle and a curved rectangle with the same style line.
42 b Each picture has a line of symmetry.
43 a Each picture contains the same size parallelogram.
44 d Each is a rotation of the same picture.
45 b Each picture contains a curved side.

46 d The others are all rotations of the same picture.
47 e The others are all rotations of the same picture.
48 e The others are all rotations of the same picture.
49 c The others are all rotations of the same picture.
50 e The others all have six stars.

Paper 3

1	b	number of line crosses same as number of sides on the shape
2	e	reflection in the vertical mirror line
3	b	rotating 90° clockwise
4	d	reflection in the vertical mirror line
5	b	shape made smaller and doubled, and stripes reflected in the vertical mirror line
6	c	inner shape becomes outer shape, outer shape becomes inner shape
7	a	rotate 90° anticlockwise
8	a	rotate 90° anticlockwise
9	c	shape becomes smaller and paler, outer line becomes thinner
10	a	rotate 90° anticlockwise
11	a	first letter – thickness of line second letter – number of sides
12	e	first letter – style of diagonal line second letter – thickness of horizontal line
13	b	first letter – number of arrows pointing in and out second letter – colour of rhombus
14	c	first letter – number of lines crossing the arrow second letter – direction of arrow
15	d	first letter – position of coloured half second letter – colour of shaded half

Paper 3 – *continued*

16 | b |

17 | b

18 | a

19 | e

20 | c

21 | c
22 | e
23 | b
24 | d
25 | c

If in doubt about the nets of cubes, copy them onto a piece of paper and fold them.

26	e	rotating 45° anticlockwise
27	d	rotating 90° clockwise
28	a	rotating 45° anticlockwise
29	d	repeating pattern
30	e	repeating pattern

31 | e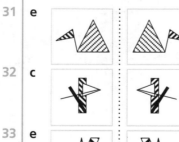

32 | c

33 | e

34 | c

35 | a

Paper 3 – *continued*

36	c	Each is a rotation of the same picture.
37	c	Each picture has a line of symmetry.
38	a	Each is a rotation of the same picture.
39	c	Each is a rotation of the same picture.
40	b	Each is a rotation of the same picture.
41	a	The others are all rotations of the same picture.
42	e	The others are all rotations of the same picture.
43	a	The others are all rotations of the same picture.
44	c	The others are all rotations of the same picture.
45	b	The others are all rotations of the same picture.

46 | d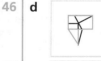

47 | c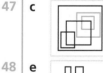

48 | e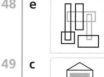

49 | c

50 | e

Paper 4

1 **b** rotating 90° anticlockwise
2 **d** rotating 90° clockwise
3 **c** reflective corners
4 **d** shapes in the first two squares of each row combine to make the third, with the middle shape reflected in the horizontal mirror line
5 **d** rotating 90° anticlockwise
6 **c** first letter – number of black circles
second letter – arrow position
7 **c** first letter – thickness of separate line
second letter – pattern direction
8 **d** first letter – number of sides of outer shape
second letter – number of lines
9 **e** first letter – pattern direction
second letter – shape position
10 **a** first letter – pattern direction
second letter – arrow position

11 **a**
12 **c**
13 **a**
14 **b**
15 **e**

Paper 4 – continued

16 **e**
17 **d**
18 **a**
19 **e**
20 **c**

If in doubt about the nets of cubes, copy them onto a piece of paper and fold them.

21 **e** rotating 180° and getting smaller
22 **b** repeating pattern
23 **e** rotating 45° anticlockwise
24 **e** rotating 45° clockwise
25 **c** number of line crosses increases by one each time

26 **c**
27 **b**
28 **c**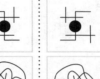
29 **a**
30 **b**

31 **a** Each is a rotation of the same picture.
32 **b** Each picture contains ten lines and a square.
33 **d** Each picture contains a multiple of three circles.
34 **a** Each is a rotation of the same picture.
35 **d** Each picture contains exactly the same four shapes.

Paper 4 – continued

36 **d** The others all contain three shapes.
37 **b** The others are all rotations of the same picture.
38 **c** The others are all rotations of the same picture.
39 **e** The others are all rotations of the same picture.
40 **e** The other shapes all have a total of eight sides.

41 **c**
42 **e**
43 **d**
44 **c**
45 **c**

46 **e** number of sides halved and lines reflected
47 **b** reflection in the vertical mirror line
48 **d** grey turns white, white turns black, black turns stripy
49 **c** half the white circles turn black
50 **b** half the number of shapes in the first picture make up the number of sides of the shape in the second picture

Paper 5

1 **b** first letter – thickness of arrow
second letter – colour

2 **c** first letter – number of circles
second letter – line thickness

3 **d** first letter – pattern
second letter – line direction

4 **c** first letter – colour of inner shape
second letter – outer shape

5 **a** first letter – line thickness
second letter – number of vertical lines

6 **e**

7 **d**

8 **b**

9 **b**

10 **c**

11 **b**
12 **d**
13 **b**
14 **e**
15 **d**

If in doubt about the nets of cubes, copy them onto a piece of paper and fold them.

Paper 5 – continued

16 **b** number of sides decreases by two each time

17 **d** the parallelogram reflects, moves down and gets paler; the lines reflect; the oval rotates 90°, moves up and gets darker

18 **a** rotating 90° anticlockwise – whilst B is very similar, note that the wiggly line is reflected

19 **d** rotating 90° clockwise
20 **b** rotating 90° clockwise

21 **c**

22 **e**

23 **a**

24 **a**

25 **c**

26 **e** Each is a rotation of the same picture (look at the small shapes carefully).

27 **c** Each is a rotation of the same picture.

28 **d** Each picture contains a curved edge.

29 **a** Each picture contains five lines.

30 **b** Each picture contains a trapezium with the wide edge on a line.

Paper 5 – continued

31 **a** The others are all rotations of the same picture.

32 **e** The others are all rotations of the same picture.

33 **b** The others all contain slanted lines.

34 **a** The others are all rotations of the same picture.

35 **b** The others are all rotations of the same picture.

36 **d**

37 **c**

38 **e**

39 **a**

40 **a**

41 **c** shape is reflected in the horizontal mirror line and the lines rotate 90°

42 **c** reflection in the vertical mirror line

43 **b** rotating 90° clockwise

44 **d** reflection in the vertical mirror line

45 **e** reflection in the vertical mirror line and black turns white

46 **d** reflective corners
47 **b** rotating 90° clockwise
48 **c** rotating 90° clockwise
49 **e** pictures in the first two squares of each row combine to make the third picture
50 **c** rotating 45° clockwise

Paper 6

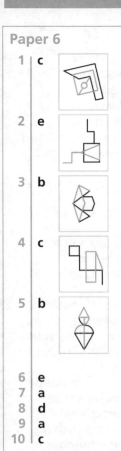

1 c
2 e
3 b
4 c
5 b
6 e
7 a
8 d
9 a
10 c

If in doubt about the nets of cubes, copy them onto a piece of paper and fold them.

11 e first letter – total number of sides of internal shape/s
second letter – number of internal shapes
12 a first letter – line position
second letter – number of stars
13 c first letter – number of sides of outer shape
second letter – outer shape line pattern
14 c first letter – inner shape fill pattern
second letter – outer shape fill pattern
15 b first letter – number of lines
second letter – number of sides of outer shape

Paper 6 – *continued*

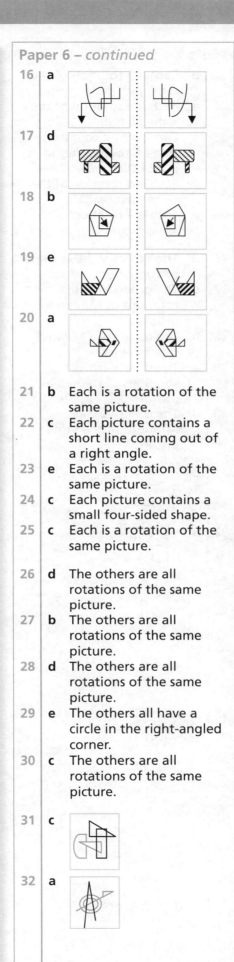

16 a
17 d
18 b
19 e
20 a

21 b Each is a rotation of the same picture.
22 c Each picture contains a short line coming out of a right angle.
23 e Each is a rotation of the same picture.
24 c Each picture contains a small four-sided shape.
25 c Each is a rotation of the same picture.
26 d The others are all rotations of the same picture.
27 b The others are all rotations of the same picture.
28 d The others are all rotations of the same picture.
29 e The others all have a circle in the right-angled corner.
30 c The others are all rotations of the same picture.
31 c
32 a

Paper 6 – *continued*

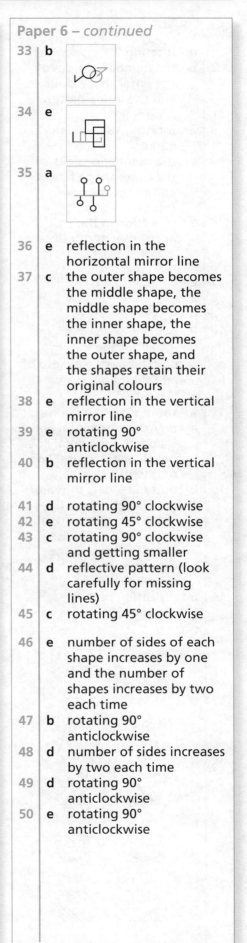

33 b
34 e
35 a
36 e reflection in the horizontal mirror line
37 c the outer shape becomes the middle shape, the middle shape becomes the inner shape, the inner shape becomes the outer shape, and the shapes retain their original colours
38 e reflection in the vertical mirror line
39 e rotating 90° anticlockwise
40 b reflection in the vertical mirror line
41 d rotating 90° clockwise
42 e rotating 45° clockwise
43 c rotating 90° clockwise and getting smaller
44 d reflective pattern (look carefully for missing lines)
45 c rotating 45° clockwise
46 e number of sides of each shape increases by one and the number of shapes increases by two each time
47 b rotating 90° anticlockwise
48 d number of sides increases by two each time
49 d rotating 90° anticlockwise
50 e rotating 90° anticlockwise

Paper 7

1	d	rotating 90° clockwise
2	b	the number of sides of the outer shape doubles and the inside pattern rotates 90°
3	a	rotating 180° and getting darker
4	c	the number of sides of the outer shape halves and the pattern is reflected
5	a	reflection in the horizontal mirror line
6	a	
7	e	
8	a	
9	d	
10	b	

If in doubt about the nets of cubes, copy them onto a piece of paper and fold them.

11	a	rotating 45° clockwise
12	a	an extra horizontal line is added, horizontal lines get thinner, vertical line gets wider
13	b	outer line gets thinner, inner lines rotate 45° clockwise, outer rhombus moves in a clockwise direction around the rounded rectangle and gets lighter
14	b	repeating pattern
15	a	rotating 90° clockwise

16	d	
17	b	
18	d	
19	b	
20	c	

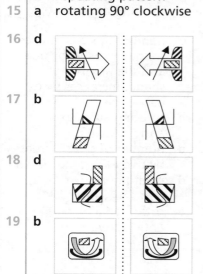

Paper 7 – continued

21	b	Each is a rotation of the same picture.
22	a	Each is a rotation of the same picture.
23	a	Each picture contains three arrows pointing out of the circle.
24	b	Each is a rotation of the same picture.
25	a	Each is a rotation of the same picture.
26	d	The others all have a line of symmetry.
27	e	The others are all rotations of the same picture.
28	b	The others are all eight-sided shapes.
29	a	The others are all rotations of the same picture.
30	d	The others are all rotations of the same picture.

31	d	
32	b	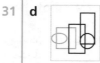
33	c	
34	e	
35	b	

Paper 7 – continued

36	a	rotating 90° anticlockwise
37	e	rotating 90° anticlockwise
38	a	reflective corners
39	d	lines rotate 90° and each row has one, two and three lines
40	e	rotating 135° clockwise
41	e	first letter – number of lines second letter – number of arrow heads
42	b	first letter – number of shapes second letter – total number of sides
43	c	first letter – fill pattern second letter – fraction shaded
44	d	first letter – number of sides of outer shape second letter – fill pattern of inner shape
45	a	first letter – number of sides of outer shape second letter – number of sides of inner shape

46	c	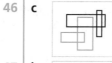
47	b	
48	d	
49	d	
50	b	

This book of answers is a pull-out section from
Non-verbal Reasoning Progress Papers 1

Published by **Schofield & Sims Ltd**
Dogley Mill, Fenay Bridge, Huddersfield HD8 0NQ, UK
Telephone 01484 607080
www.schofieldandsims.co.uk

First published in 2016
This edition copyright © Schofield & Sims Ltd, 2018

Author: **Rebecca Brant**
Rebecca Brant has asserted her moral rights under the Copyright, Designs and
Patents Act, 1988, to be identified as the author of this work.

British Library Cataloguing in Publication Data
A catalogue record for this book is available from the British Library.

Design by **Oxford Designers & Illustrators**
Printed in the UK by **Page Bros (Norwich) Ltd**

ISBN 978 07217 1460 8

MARK
✓ OR ✗

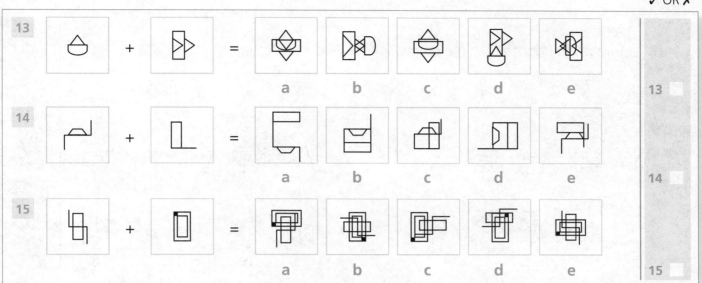

13 | | 13
14 | | 14
15 | | 15

Q. 16–20 Nets of cubes

Which net can be made exactly from the cube? Circle the letter.

Which cube can be made exactly from the net? Circle the letter.

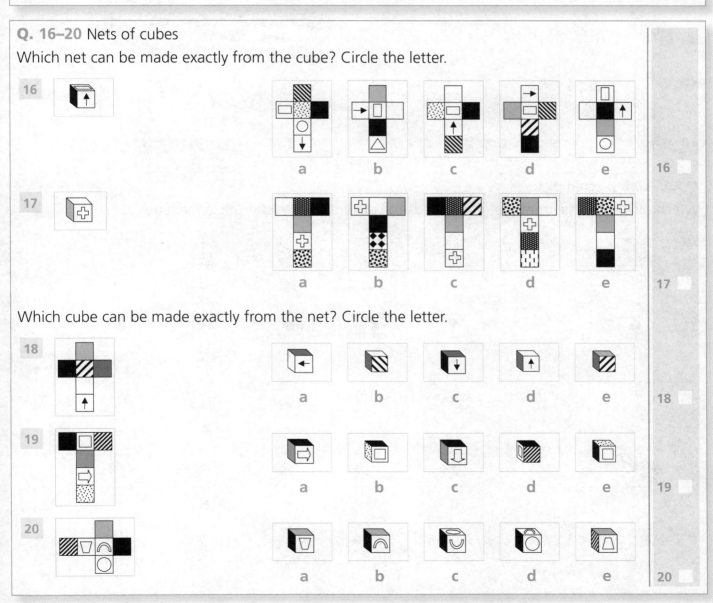

16 | | 16
17 | | 17
18 | | 18
19 | | 19
20 | | 20

MARK

MARK
✓ OR ✗

Q. 21–25 Series

Which picture on the right fits in the empty space? Circle the letter.

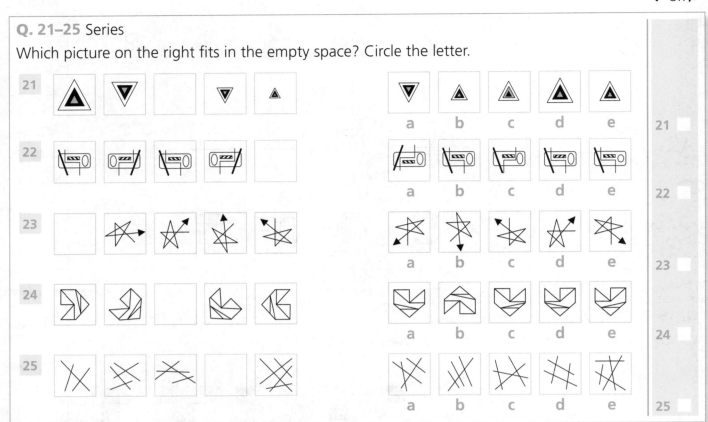

Q. 26–30 Reflected pictures

Which picture on the right is a reflection of the picture on the left? Circle the letter.

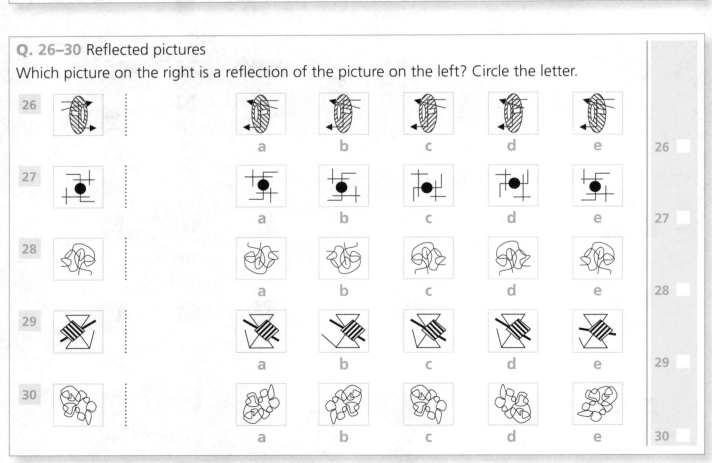

MARK

Schofield & Sims • Non-verbal Reasoning Progress Papers 1

MARK
✓ OR ✗

Q. 31–35 Similarities

Which picture on the right belongs to the group on the left? Circle the letter.

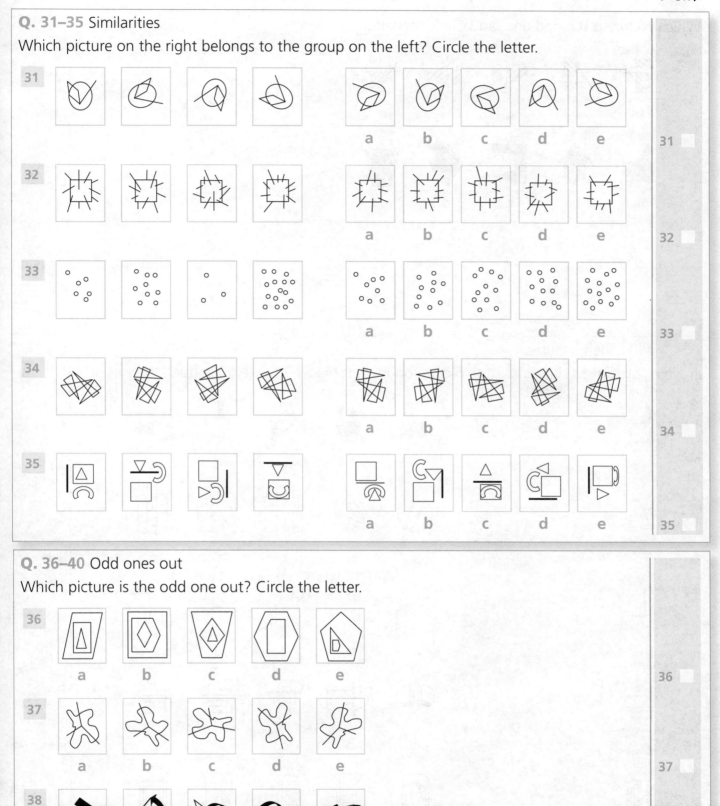

a   b   c   d   e

31   32   33   34   35

Q. 36–40 Odd ones out

Which picture is the odd one out? Circle the letter.

36   a   b   c   d   e

37   a   b   c   d   e

38   a   b   c   d   e

36   37   38

MARK

MARK
✓ OR ✗

Which picture is the odd one out? Circle the letter.

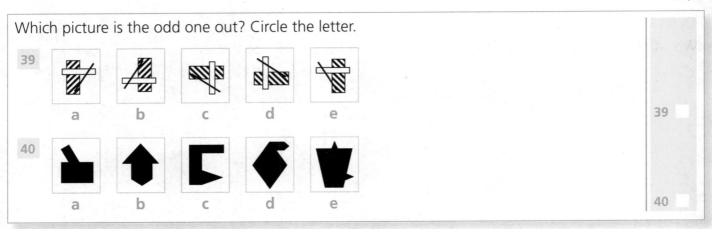

39
a   b   c   d   e

39 ☐

40
a   b   c   d   e

40 ☐

Q. 41–45 Hidden pictures
In which picture on the right is the picture on the left hidden? Circle the letter.

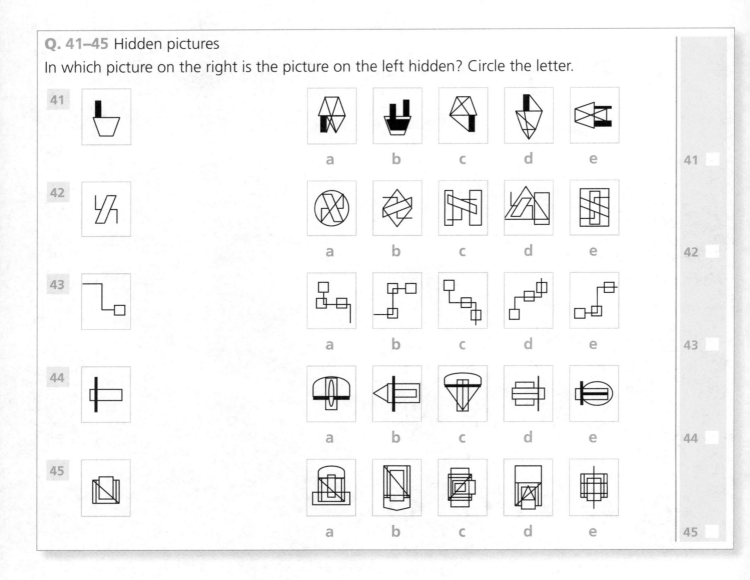

41
a   b   c   d   e   41 ☐

42
a   b   c   d   e   42 ☐

43
a   b   c   d   e   43 ☐

44
a   b   c   d   e   44 ☐

45
a   b   c   d   e   45 ☐

MARK ☐

Schofield & Sims • Non-verbal Reasoning Progress Papers 1

MARK
✓ OR ✗

Q. 46–50 Analogies

Which of the five pictures on the right goes with the third one to make a pair like the two on the left? Circle the letter.

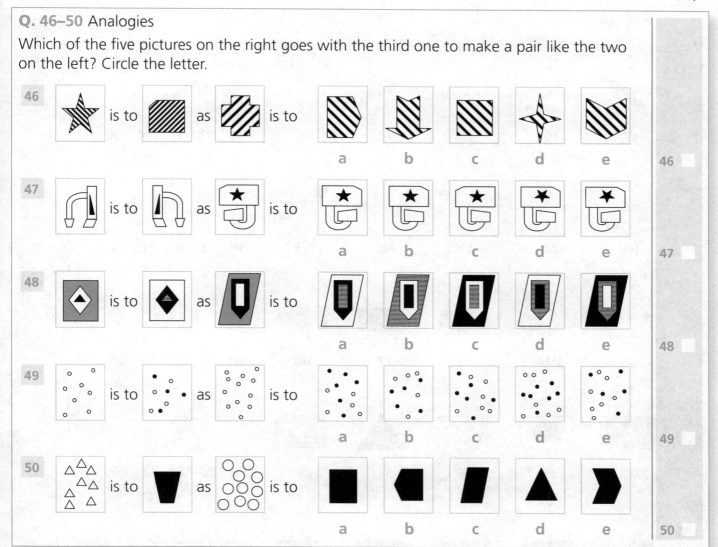

46   a   b   c   d   e   46 ☐

47   a   b   c   d   e   47 ☐

48   a   b   c   d   e   48 ☐

49   a   b   c   d   e   49 ☐

50   a   b   c   d   e   50 ☐

MARK ☐

END OF TEST

PAPER 4 TOTAL MARK ☐

Q. 1–5 Codes
What is the code of the final picture? Circle the letter.

1

YQ	PZ	LK	FJ	PK	PQ	YZ	LI	PK	YK
					a	b	c	d	e

1 ☐

2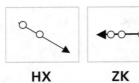

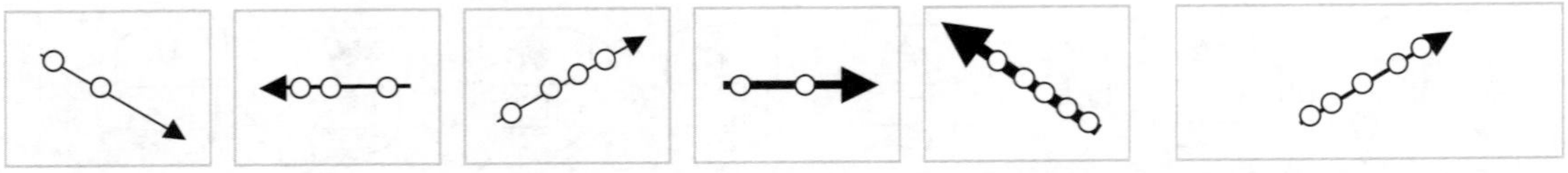

HX	ZK	TX	HL	WE	HK	TE	WK	ZE	WX
					a	b	c	d	e

2 ☐

3

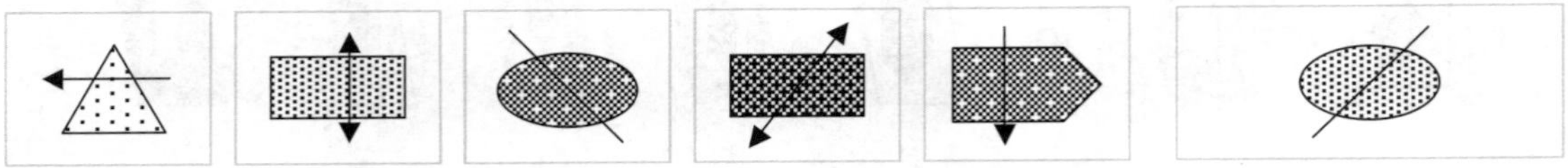

GH	DM	AS	YT	AM	AH	AT	YS	DT	DS
					a	b	c	d	e

3 ☐

4

GF	ER	GP	SJ	LR	SR	GF	EJ	LF	EP
					a	b	c	d	e

4 ☐

5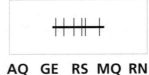

AS	RE	MN	GN	RQ	AQ	GE	RS	MQ	RN
					a	b	c	d	e

5 ☐

Q. 6–10 Combined pictures
Which picture on the right can be made by combining the first two pictures? Circle the letter.

6 + =

        a   b   c   d   e

6 ☐

7 + =

        a   b   c   d   e

7 ☐

MARK ☐

MARK
✓ OR ✗

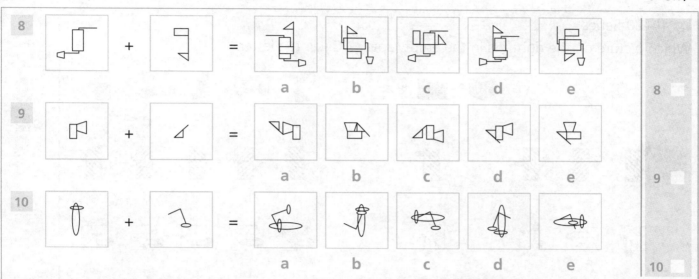

8

9

10

Q. 11–15 Nets of cubes

Which net can be made exactly from the cube? Circle the letter.

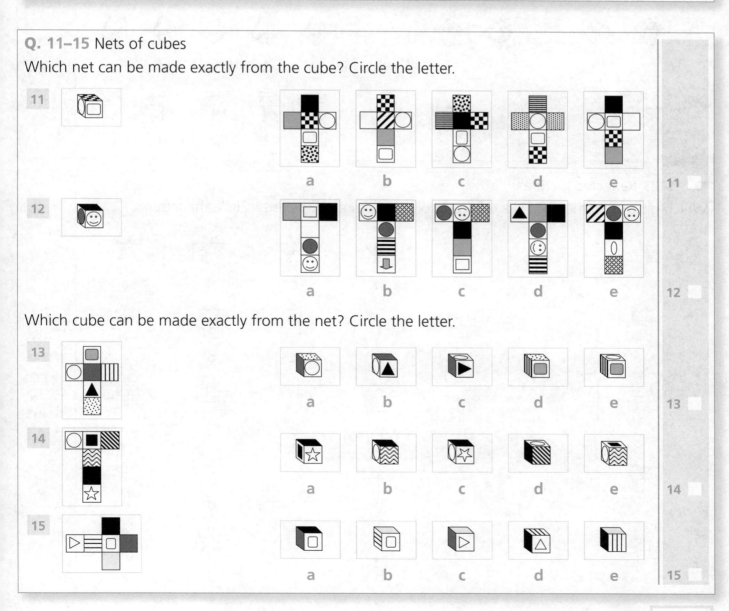

Which cube can be made exactly from the net? Circle the letter.

11

12

13

14

15

MARK

MARK
✓ OR ✗

Q. 16–20 Series

Which picture on the right fits in the empty space? Circle the letter.

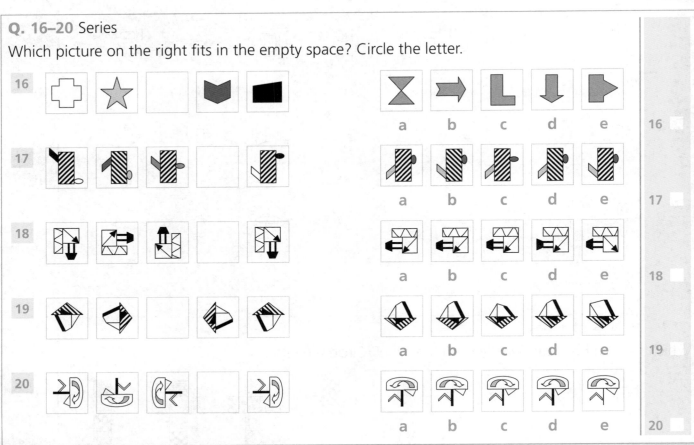

16
a   b   c   d   e   16

17
a   b   c   d   e   17

18
a   b   c   d   e   18

19
a   b   c   d   e   19

20
a   b   c   d   e   20

Q. 21–25 Reflected pictures

Which picture on the right is a reflection of the picture on the left? Circle the letter.

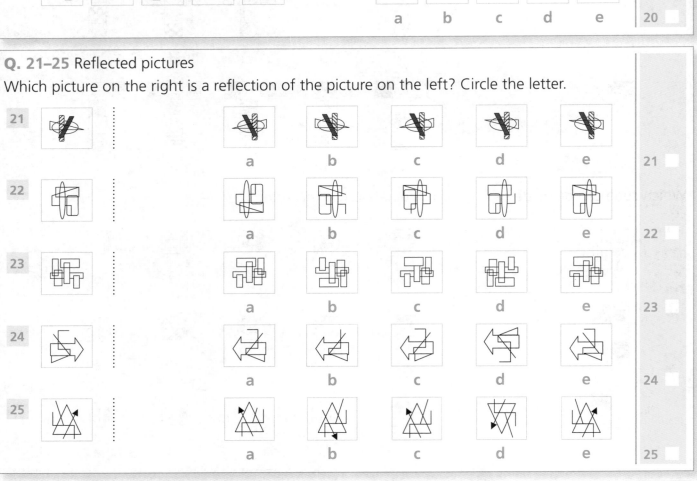

21
a   b   c   d   e   21

22
a   b   c   d   e   22

23
a   b   c   d   e   23

24
a   b   c   d   e   24

25
a   b   c   d   e   25

MARK

MARK
✓ OR ✗

Q. 26–30 Similarities

Which picture on the right belongs to the group on the left? Circle the letter.

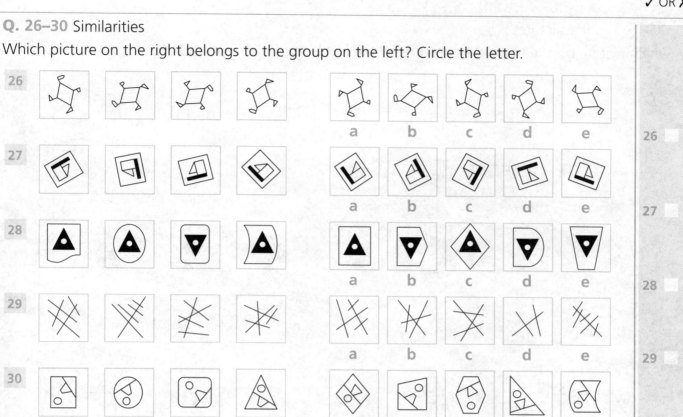

26 ☐

27 ☐

28 ☐

29 ☐

30 ☐

Q. 31–35 Odd ones out

Which picture is the odd one out? Circle the letter.

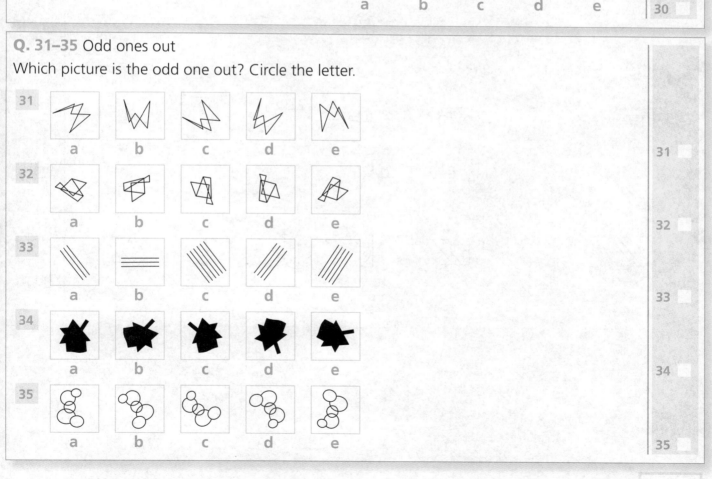

31 ☐

32 ☐

33 ☐

34 ☐

35 ☐

MARK ☐

MARK
✓ OR ✗

Q. 36–40 Hidden pictures

In which picture on the right is the picture on the left hidden? Circle the letter.

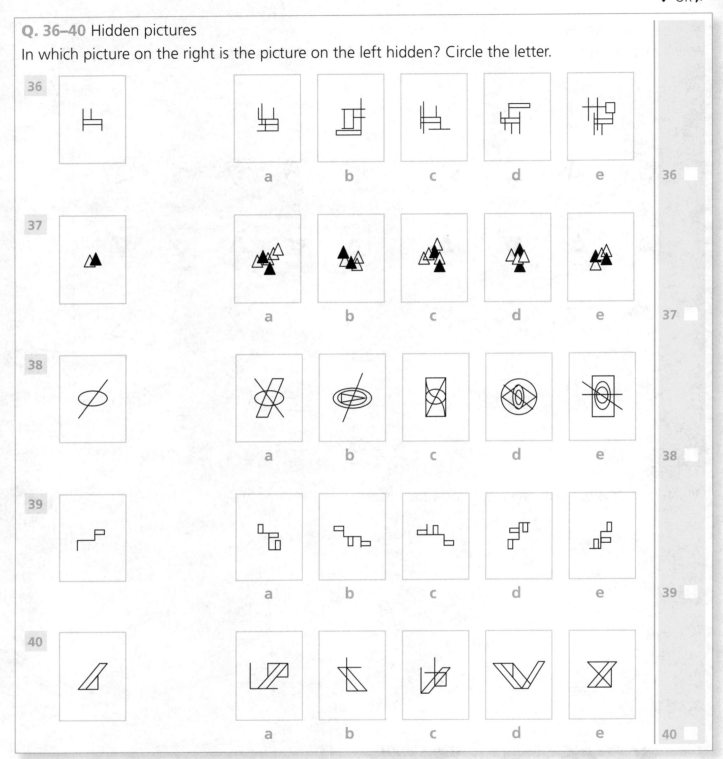

36

a   b   c   d   e   36

37

a   b   c   d   e   37

38

a   b   c   d   e   38

39

a   b   c   d   e   39

40

a   b   c   d   e   40

MARK

MARK
✓ OR ✗

Q. 41–45 Analogies

Which of the five pictures on the right goes with the third one to make a pair like the two on the left? Circle the letter.

41 is to as is to

                                      a   b   c   d   e   **41** ☐

42 is to as is to

                                        a   b   c   d   e   **42** ☐

43 is to as is to

                                        a   b   c   d   e   **43** ☐

44 is to as is to

                                        a   b   c   d   e   **44** ☐

45 is to as is to

                                        a   b   c   d   e   **45** ☐

MARK

MARK
✓ OR ✗

Q. 46–50 Matrices

Which picture on the right best fits into the space in the grid? Circle the letter.

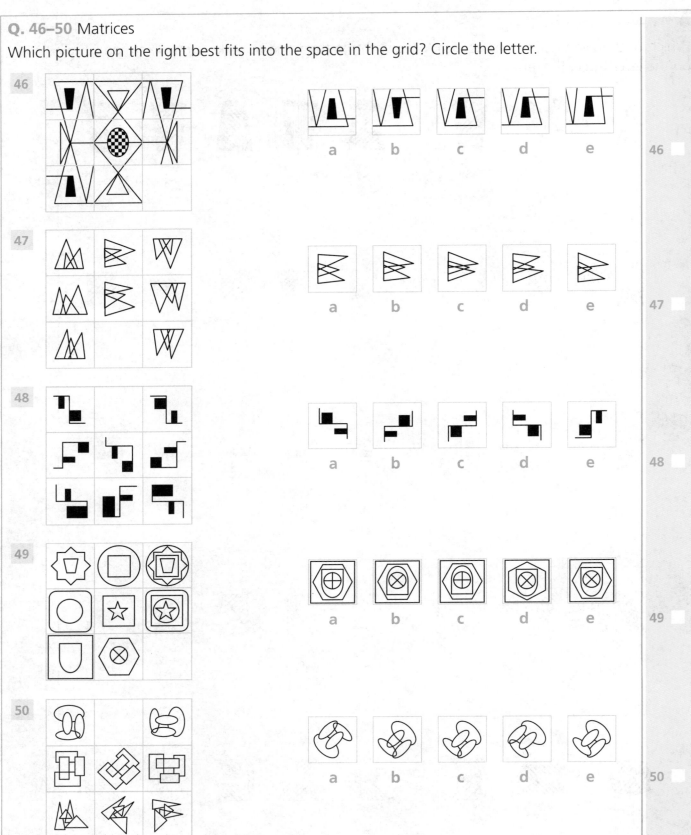

46 |
47 |
48 |
49 |
50 |

MARK

PAPER 5 TOTAL MARK

START HERE

MARK
✓ OR ✗

Q. 1–5 Combined pictures

Which picture on the right can be made by combining the first two pictures? Circle the letter.

1   +   =

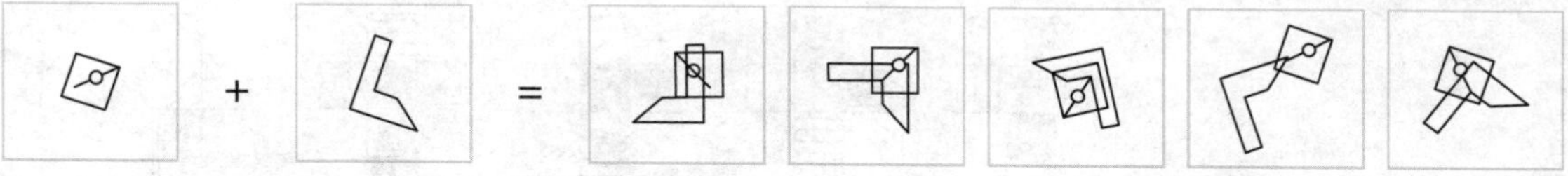

                               a   b   c   d   e   1

2   +   ⃞   =

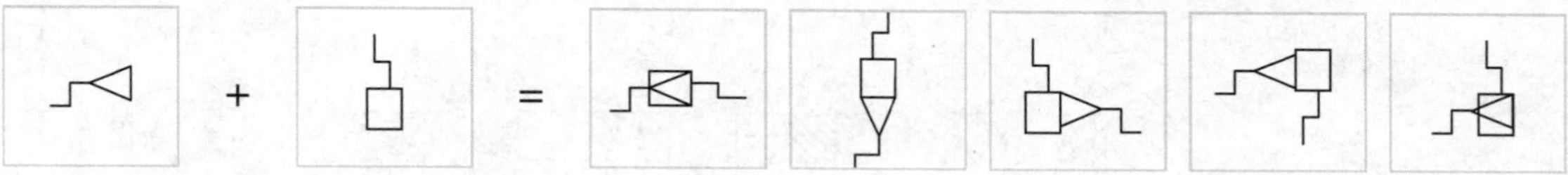

                               a   b   c   d   e   2

3   +   ⃞   =

                               a   b   c   d   e   3

4   +   ⃞   =

                               a   b   c   d   e   4

5   +   ⃞   =   ⃞   ⃞   ⃞   ⃞   ⃞

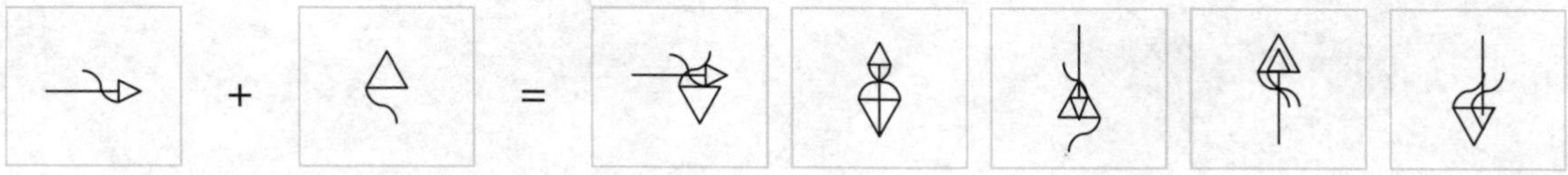

                               a   b   c   d   e   5

MARK [ ]

Q. 6–10 Nets of cubes

Which net can be made exactly from the cube? Circle the letter.

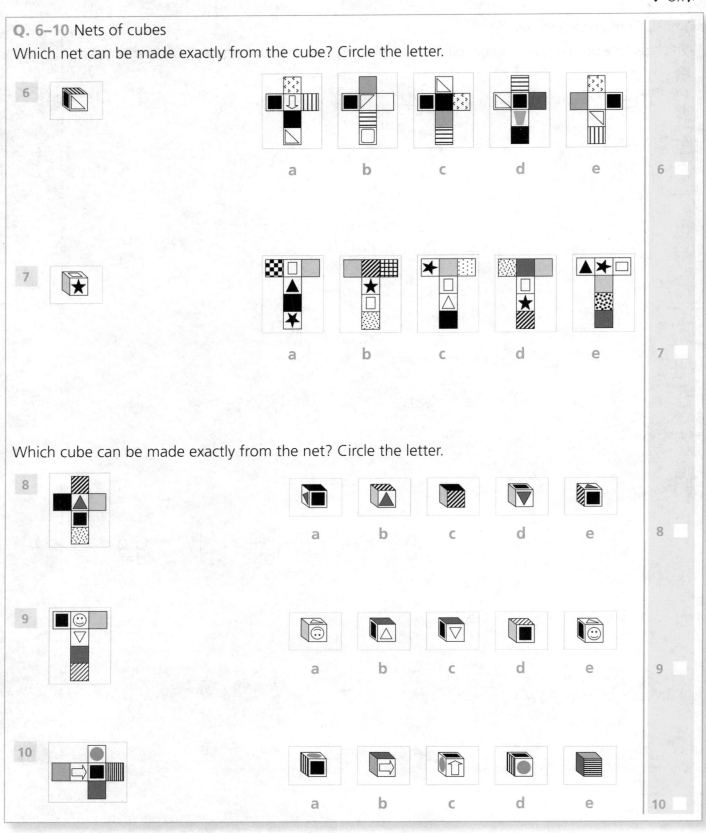

6   a   b   c   d   e   6

7   a   b   c   d   e   7

Which cube can be made exactly from the net? Circle the letter.

8   a   b   c   d   e   8

9   a   b   c   d   e   9

10   a   b   c   d   e   10

MARK

MARK
✓ OR ✗

Q. 11–15 Codes

What is the code of the final picture? Circle the letter.

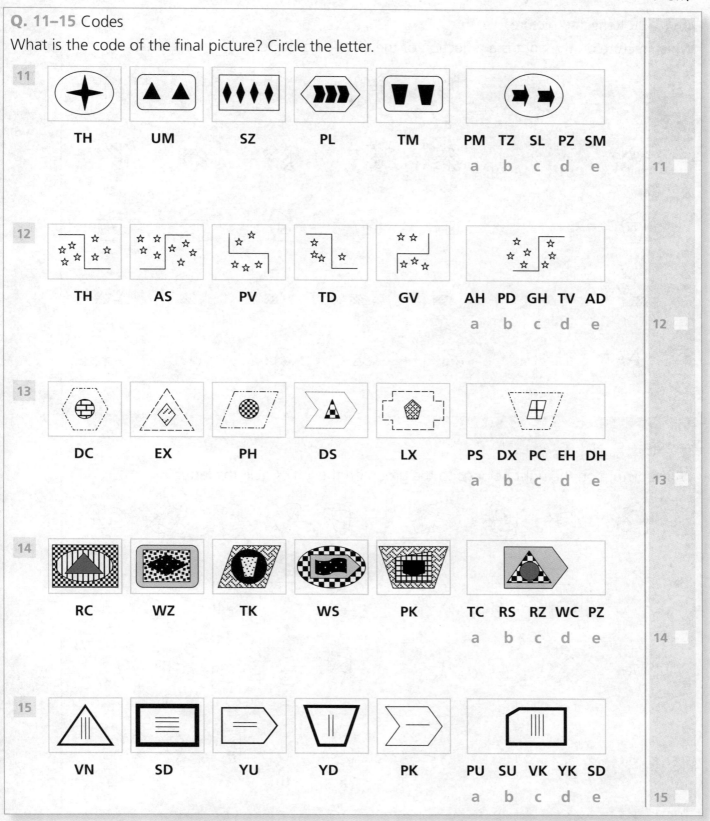

11

TH UM SZ PL TM

PM TZ SL PZ SM
a   b   c   d   e

11 ☐

12

TH AS PV TD GV

AH PD GH TV AD
a   b   c   d   e

12 ☐

13

DC EX PH DS LX

PS DX PC EH DH
a   b   c   d   e

13 ☐

14

RC WZ TK WS PK

TC RS RZ WC PZ
a   b   c   d   e

14 ☐

15

VN SD YU YD PK

PU SU VK YK SD
a   b   c   d   e

15 ☐

MARK ☐

MARK
✓ OR ✗

Q. 16–20 Reflected pictures

Which picture on the right is a reflection of the picture on the left? Circle the letter.

16

a   b   c   d   e   16 ☐

17

a   b   c   d   e   17 ☐

18

a   b   c   d   e   18 ☐

19

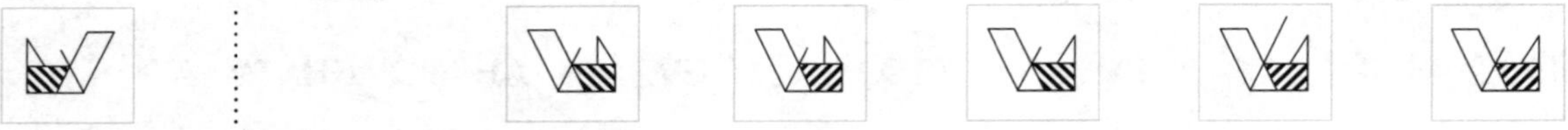

a   b   c   d   e   19 ☐

20

a   b   c   d   e   20 ☐

Q. 21–25 Similarities

Which picture on the right belongs to the group on the left? Circle the letter.

21

a   b   c   d   e   21 ☐

22

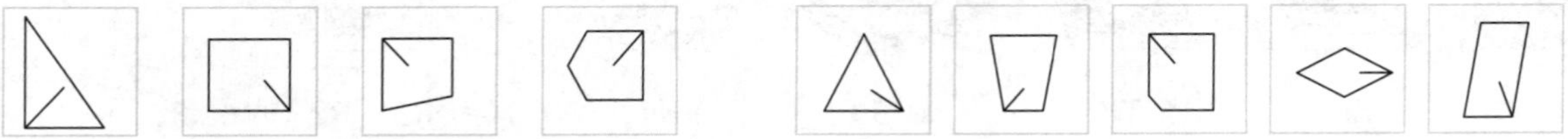

a   b   c   d   e   22 ☐

23

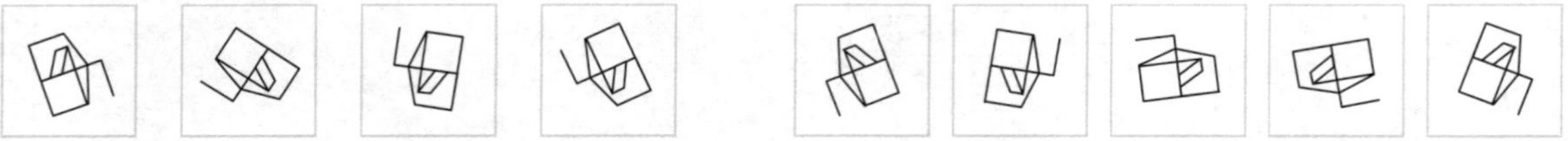

a   b   c   d   e   23 ☐

24

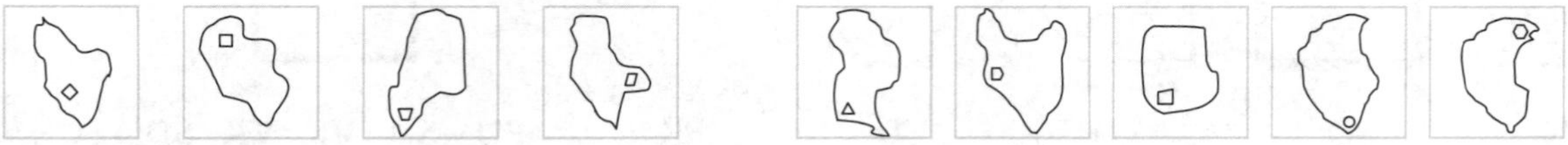

a   b   c   d   e   24 ☐

25

a   b   c   d   e   25 ☐

MARK ☐

MARK
✓ OR ✗

Q. 26–30 Odd ones out

Which picture is the odd one out? Circle the letter.

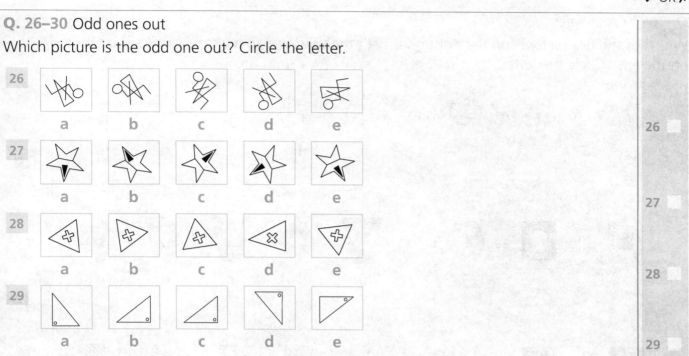

26   a   b   c   d   e

27   a   b   c   d   e

28   a   b   c   d   e

29   a   b   c   d   e

30   a   b   c   d   e

26	☐
27	☐
28	☐
29	☐
30	☐

Q. 31–35 Hidden pictures

In which picture on the right is the picture on the left hidden? Circle the letter.

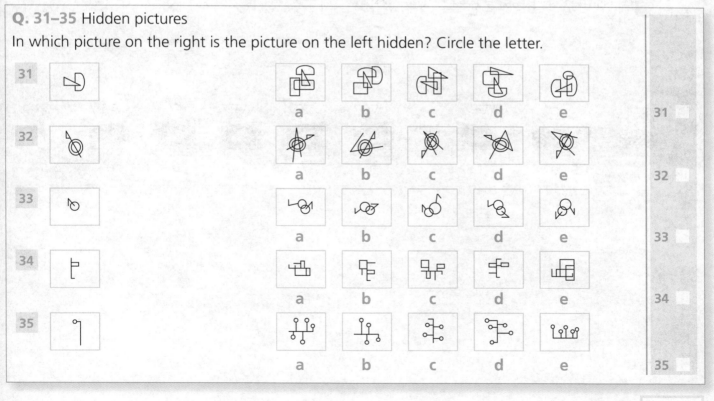

31   a   b   c   d   e

32   a   b   c   d   e

33   a   b   c   d   e

34   a   b   c   d   e

35   a   b   c   d   e

31	☐
32	☐
33	☐
34	☐
35	☐

MARK ☐

Q. 36–40 Analogies

Which of the five pictures on the right goes with the third one to make a pair like the two on the left? Circle the letter.

36 is to  as  is to
    a   b   c   d   e   36 ☐

37 is to  as  is to
    a   b   c   d   e   37 ☐

38 is to as is to

    a   b   c   d   e   38 ☐

39 is to  as  is to
    a   b   c   d   e   39 ☐

40   is to  as    is to
    a   b   c   d   e   40 ☐

MARK ☐

MARK
✓ OR ✗

Q. 41–45 Matrices

Which picture on the right best fits into the space in the grid? Circle the letter.

41

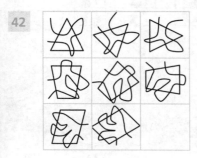
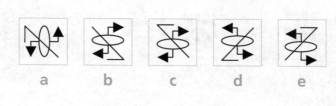

a   b   c   d   e

41 ☐

42

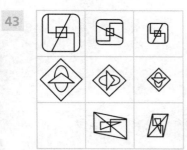
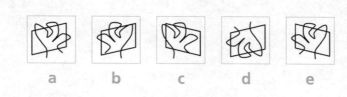

a   b   c   d   e

42 ☐

43

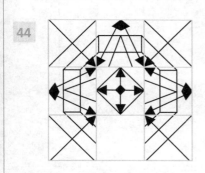
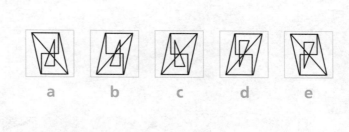

a   b   c   d   e

43 ☐

44

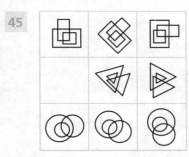
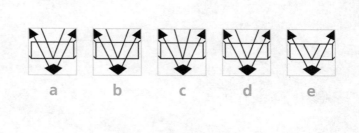

a   b   c   d   e

44 ☐

45

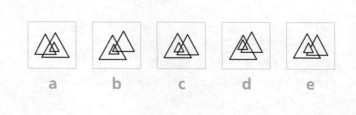

a   b   c   d   e

45 ☐

MARK ☐

MARK
✓ OR ✗

Q. 46–50 Series

Which picture on the right fits in the empty space? Circle the letter.

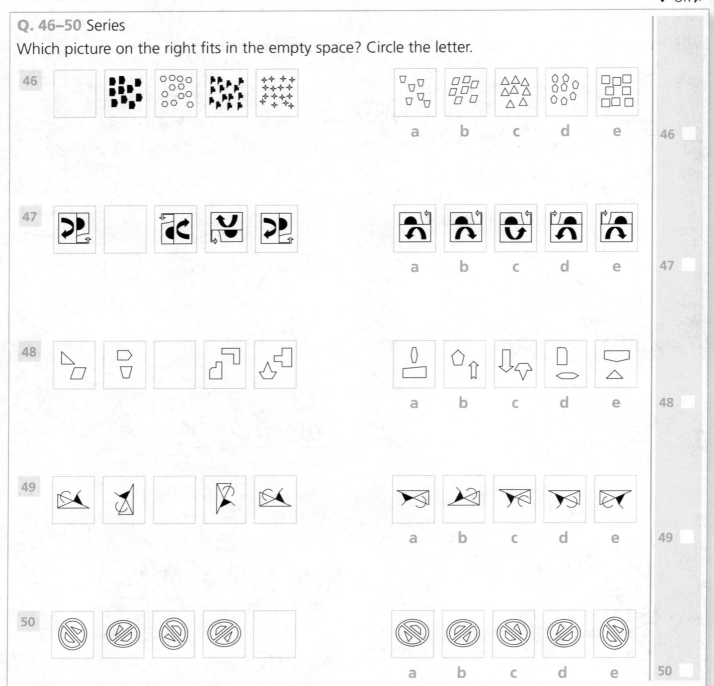

46

a   b   c   d   e   46 ☐

47

a   b   c   d   e   47 ☐

48

a   b   c   d   e   48 ☐

49

a   b   c   d   e   49 ☐

50

a   b   c   d   e   50 ☐

MARK ☐

END OF TEST

PAPER 6 TOTAL MARK ☐

START HERE

Q. 1–5 Analogies

Which of the five pictures on the right goes with the third one to make a pair like the two on the left? Circle the letter.

1 is to as is to

                                    a   b   c   d   e   **1** □

2 is to as  is to

                                    a   b   c   d   e   **2** □

3 is to as is to

                                    a   b   c   d   e   **3** □

4 is to as is to

                                    a   b   c   d   e   **4** □

5 is to as is to

                                    a   b   c   d   e   **5** □

Q. 6–10 Nets of cubes

Which net can be made exactly from the cube? Circle the letter.

6   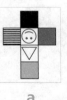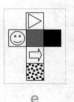

                                  a   b   c   d   e   **6** □

7   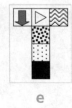

                                  a   b   c   d   e   **7** □

MARK

MARK
✓ OR ✗

Which cube can be made exactly from the net? Circle the letter.

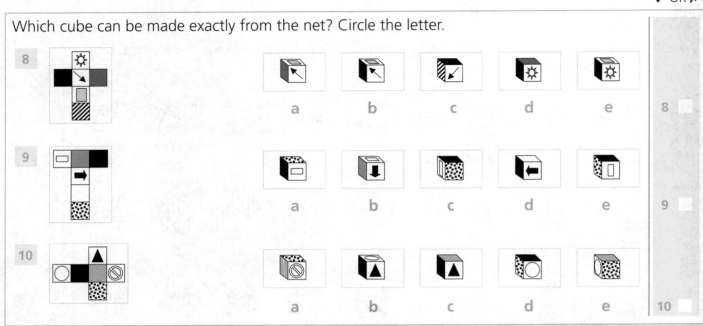

	a	b	c	d	e	
8						8
9						9
10						10

Q. 11–15 Series

Which picture on the right fits in the empty space? Circle the letter.

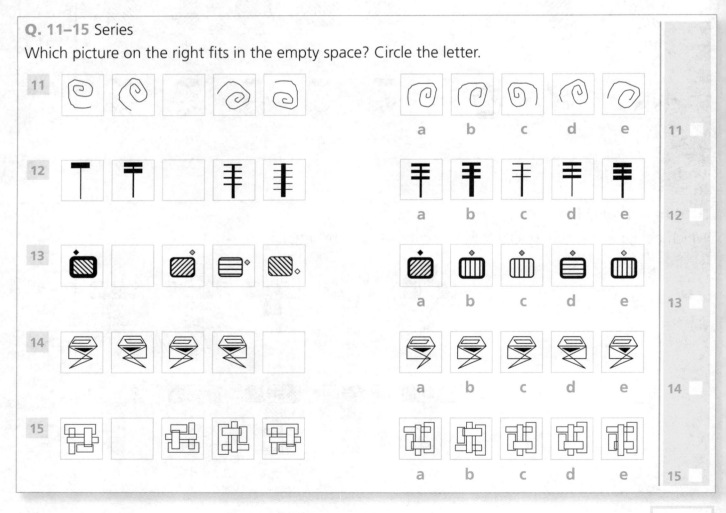

	a	b	c	d	e	
11						11
12						12
13						13
14						14
15						15

MARK

Schofield & Sims • Non-verbal Reasoning Progress Papers 1

MARK
✓ OR ✗

Q. 16–20 Reflected pictures
Which picture on the right is a reflection of the picture on the left? Circle the letter.

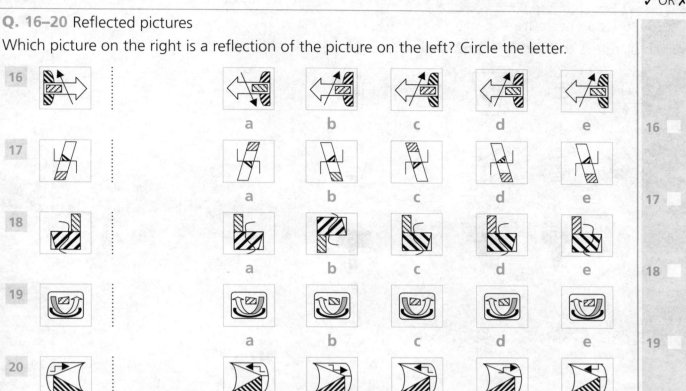

16

a   b   c   d   e

17

a   b   c   d   e

18

a   b   c   d   e

19

a   b   c   d   e

20

a   b   c   d   e

16
17
18
19
20

Q. 21–25 Similarities
Which picture on the right belongs to the group on the left? Circle the letter.

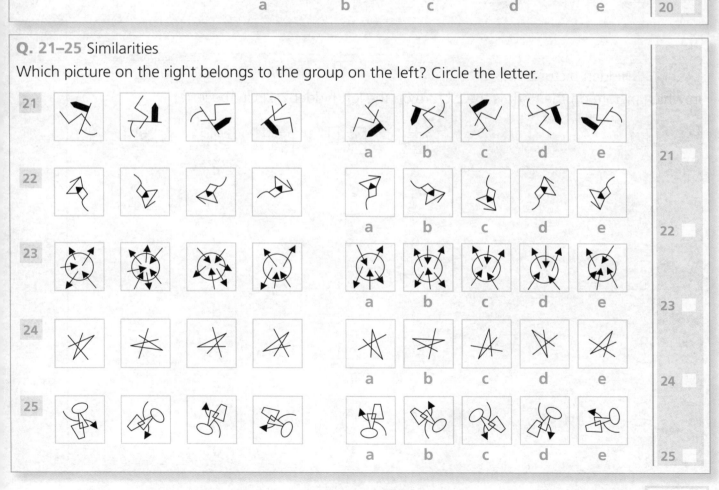

21

a   b   c   d   e

22

a   b   c   d   e

23

a   b   c   d   e

24

a   b   c   d   e

25

a   b   c   d   e

21
22
23
24
25

MARK

MARK
✓ OR ✗

Q. 26–30 Odd ones out

Which picture is the odd one out? Circle the letter.

26
   a   b   c   d   e   26 ☐

27
   a   b   c   d   e   27 ☐

28
   a   b   c   d   e   28 ☐

29
   a   b   c   d   e   29 ☐

30
   a   b   c   d   e   30 ☐

Q. 31–35 Hidden pictures

In which picture on the right is the picture on the left hidden? Circle the letter.

31 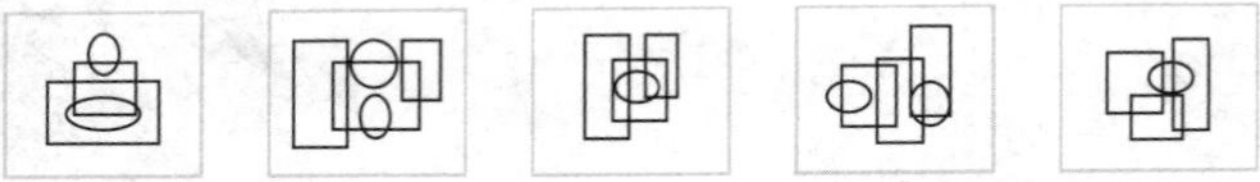 
                     a   b   c   d   e   31 ☐

32 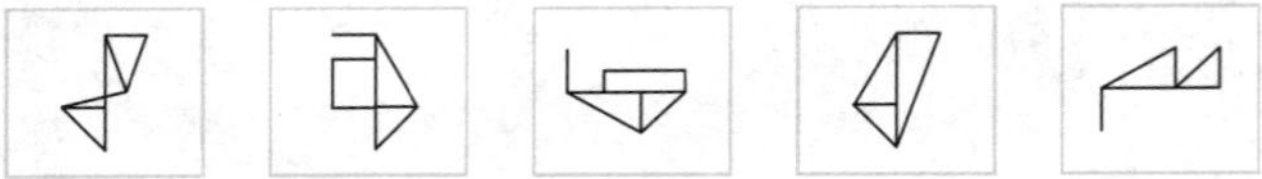 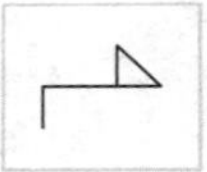
                     a   b   c   d   e   32 ☐

33  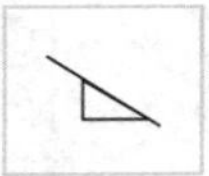   
                     a   b   c   d   e   33 ☐

34 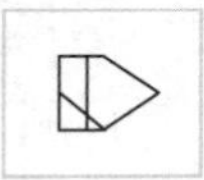
                     a   b   c   d   e   34 ☐

35 
                     a   b   c   d   e   35 ☐

MARK ☐

MARK
✓ OR ✗

Q. 36–40 Matrices

Which picture on the right best fits into the space in the grid? Circle the letter.

36

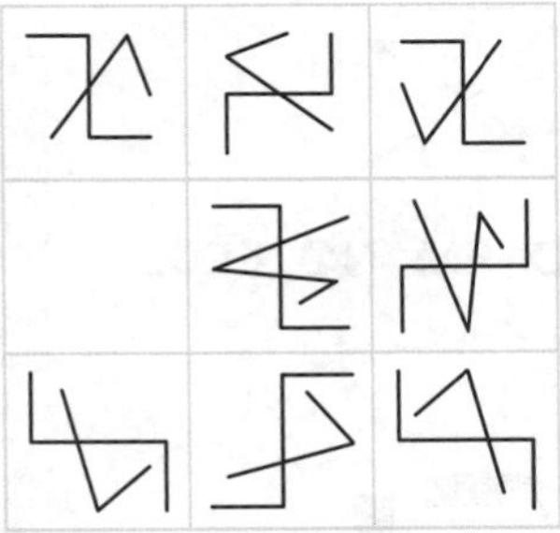

a   b   c   d   e

36 ☐

37

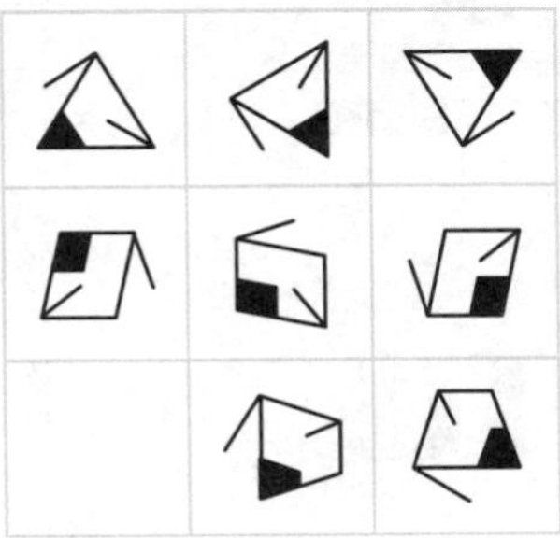

a   b   c   d   e

37 ☐

38

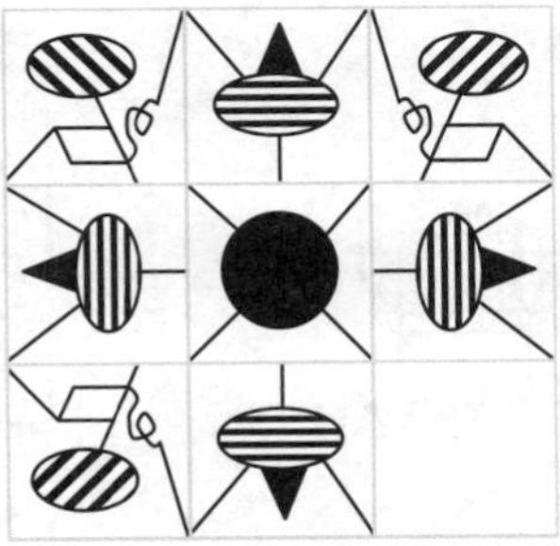

a   b   c   d   e

38 ☐

39

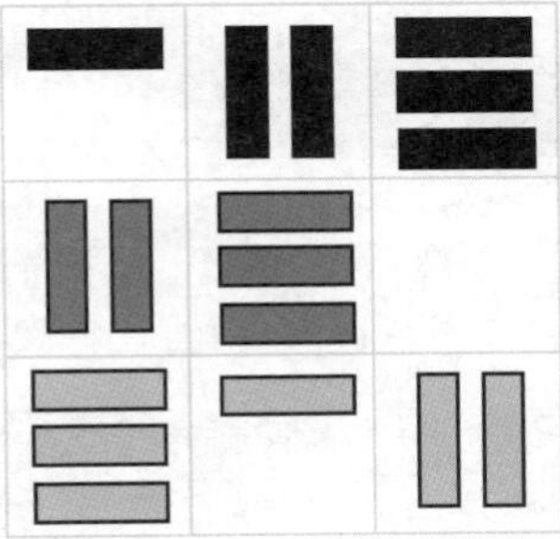

a   b   c   d   e

39 ☐

40

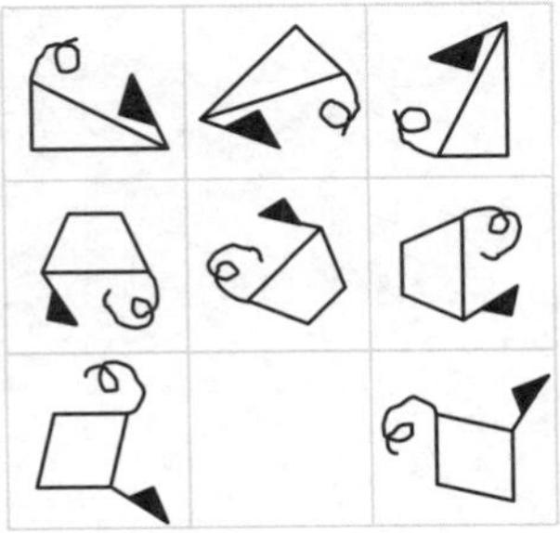

a   b   c   d   e

40 ☐

MARK ☐

MARK
✓ OR ✗

Q. 41–45 Codes

What is the code of the final picture? Circle the letter.

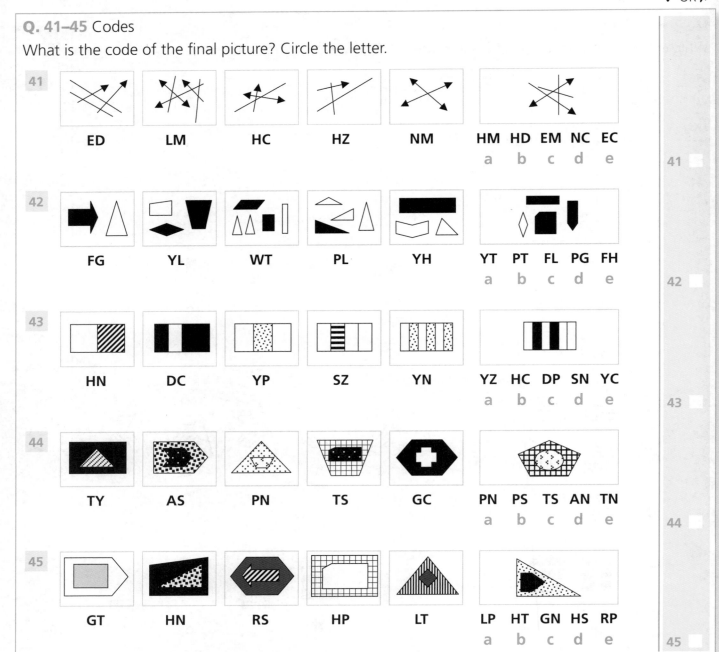

41

ED   LM   HC   HZ   NM

HM HD EM NC EC
a   b   c   d   e

41 ☐

42

FG   YL   WT   PL   YH

YT PT FL PG FH
a   b   c   d   e

42 ☐

43

HN   DC   YP   SZ   YN

YZ HC DP SN YC
a   b   c   d   e

43 ☐

44

TY   AS   PN   TS   GC

PN PS TS AN TN
a   b   c   d   e

44 ☐

45

GT   HN   RS   HP   LT

LP HT GN HS RP
a   b   c   d   e

45 ☐

MARK ☐

MARK
✓ OR ✗

Q. 46–50 Combined pictures

Which picture on the right can be made by combining the first two pictures? Circle the letter.

46   + = a b c d e

46 ☐

47   + ☐ = a b c d e

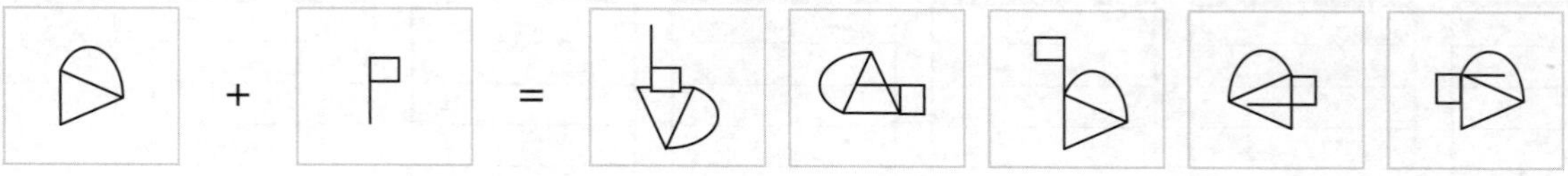

47 ☐

48   + ☐ =
a b c d e

48 ☐

49   + ☐ =
a b c d e

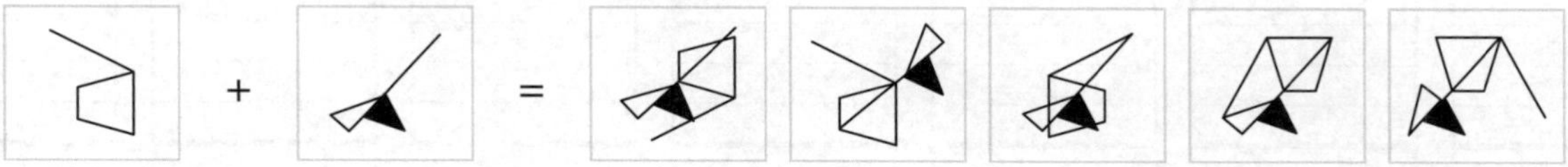

49 ☐

50   + ☐ =
a b c d e

50 ☐

MARK ☐

END OF TEST

PAPER 7 TOTAL MARK ☐

Progress chart

Write the score (out of 50) for each paper in the box provided at the bottom of the chart. Then colour in the column above the box to the appropriate height to represent this score.

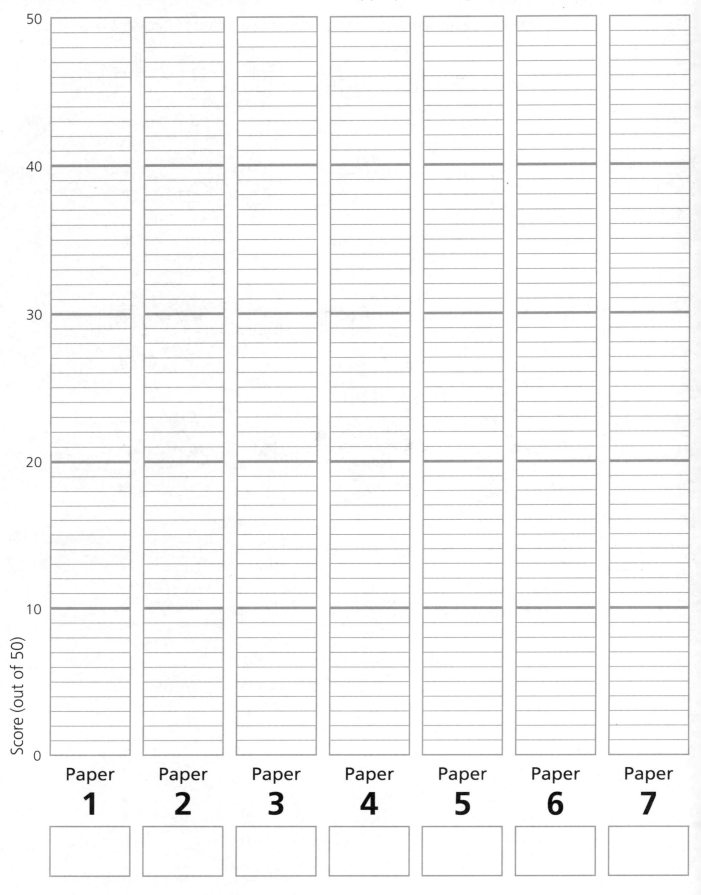